BRILLIANT BRAIN GAMES

First published by Parragon in 2008

Parragon
Queen Street House
4 Queen Street
Bath BA1 1HE, UK

ISBN: 978-1-4075-3507-4

Created and Produced by David Etherington Design
www.davidetheringtondesign.com

Design: David Etherington, Luke Griffin

Printed in China

GUY CAMPBELL
PAUL MORAN

Bath · New York · Singapore · Hong Kong · Cologne · Delhi · Melbourne

INTRODUCTION

We know the importance of keeping our bodies in shape and living a healthy lifestyle, so we take the stairs to ensure our heart gets a good work out and think nothing of the occasional round of sit-ups to keep our stomachs trim. However we often overlook the importance of caring for one of the most important organs in the body – the brain!

Brilliant Brain Games addresses this in a fun and enjoyable way by providing a fascinating journey through puzzles which will test and exercise your mind for peak mental fitness. This book will give you a thorough cerebral work out as you take on the challenge of a wide range of puzzles including logic tests, number games, picture puzzles and lateral thinking riddles.

In addition to these intellectual exercises, many of the daily puzzle entries come complete with a fascinating fact from the fields of arts, history and science, and an accompanying quote to inform and inspire you. The authors of these words of wisdom are philosophers, scientists, writers and some of the greatest minds from history including Winston Churchill, Oscar Wilde, Virginia Woolf and Irving Berlin to name but a few.

So in the pages ahead, tackle the puzzles, study the facts and be inspired by the quotes – and then reap the rewards of an exercised and mentally agile mind.

"I consider that a man's brain originally is like a little empty attic, and you have to stock it with such furniture as you choose."

ARTHUR CONAN DOYLE

HOW TO USE THIS BOOK

***Brilliant Brain Games* is uniquely devised to give you the complete mental workout, providing challenging puzzles, as well as fascinating facts and interesting quotes to inform and inspire.**

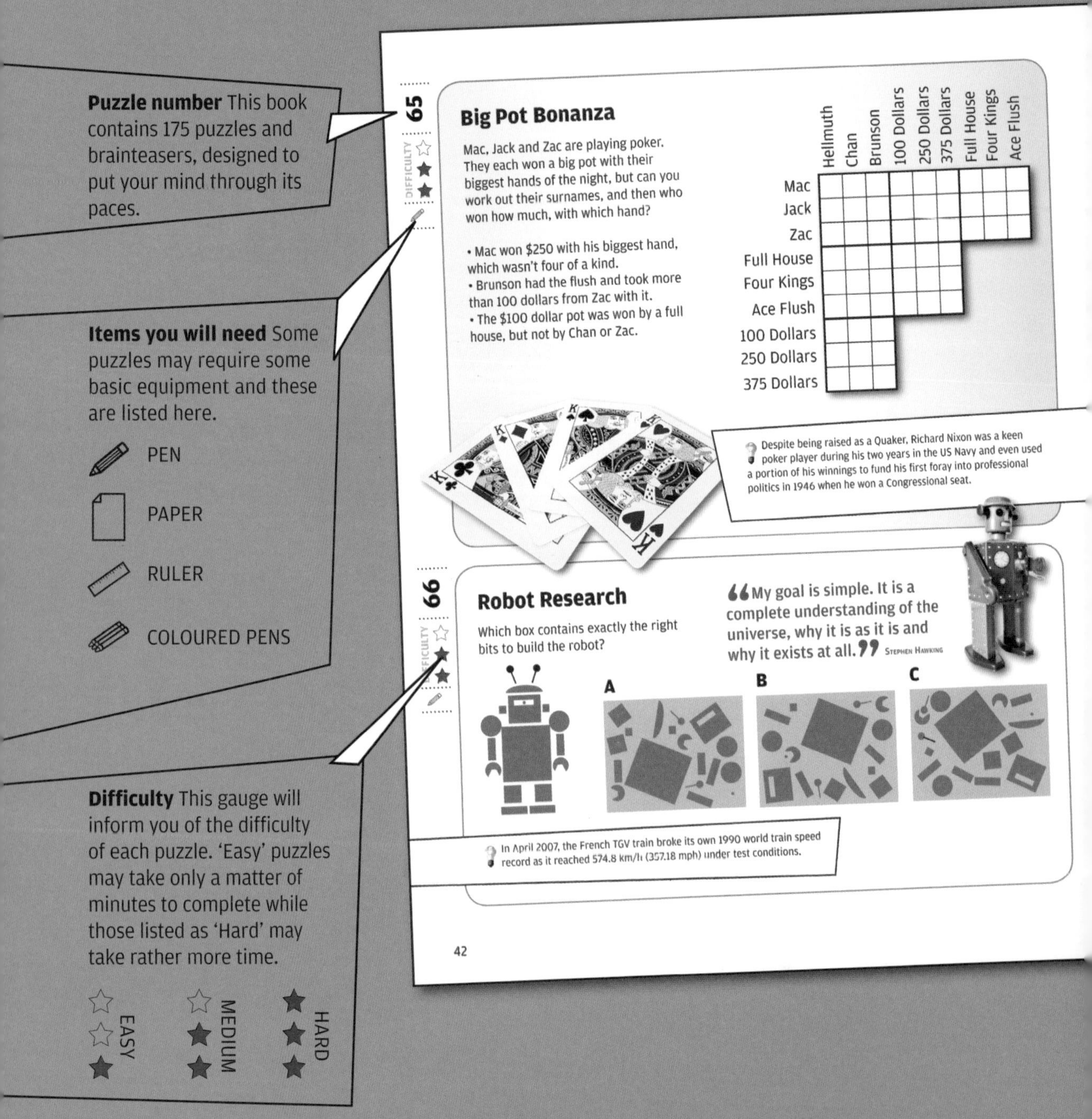

Puzzle number This book contains 175 puzzles and brainteasers, designed to put your mind through its paces.

Items you will need Some puzzles may require some basic equipment and these are listed here.

- PEN
- PAPER
- RULER
- COLOURED PENS

Difficulty This gauge will inform you of the difficulty of each puzzle. 'Easy' puzzles may take only a matter of minutes to complete while those listed as 'Hard' may take rather more time.

EASY

MEDIUM

HARD

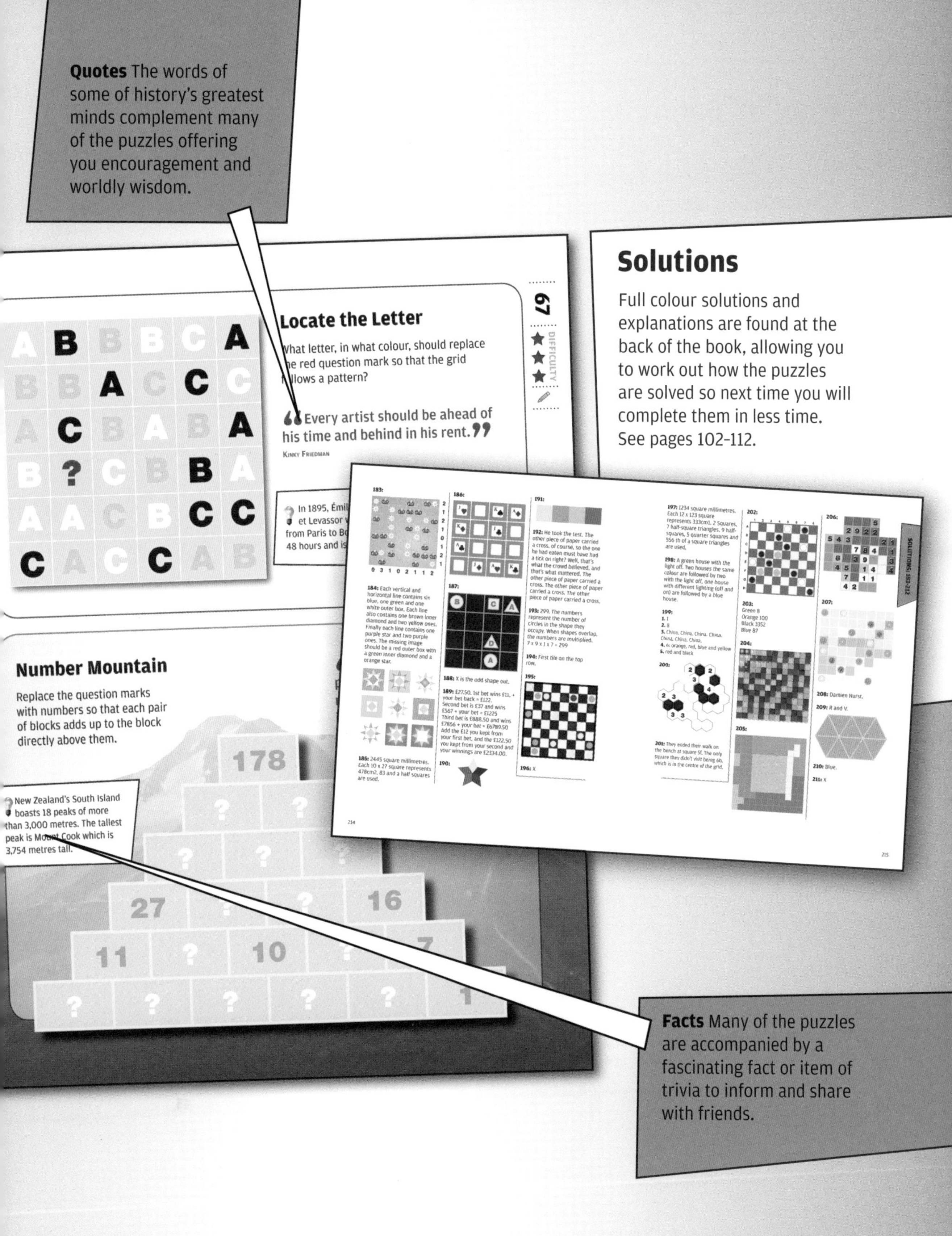

Quotes The words of some of history's greatest minds complement many of the puzzles offering you encouragement and worldly wisdom.

Solutions

Full colour solutions and explanations are found at the back of the book, allowing you to work out how the puzzles are solved so next time you will complete them in less time. See pages 102–112.

Facts Many of the puzzles are accompanied by a fascinating fact or item of trivia to inform and share with friends.

Pirate Hunter

Flintlock Freddy is an inveterate pirate sought throughout the seven seas for 50 counts of villainy. He wears a bandana and an eyepatch, but he doesn't have a beard or a hook. Can you clap your eyes on the rogue?

> "One secret of success in life is for a man to be ready for his opportunity when it comes."
>
> BENJAMIN DISRAELI

The Maldives are made up of 1,192 islands. Only 199 are inhabited and out of this figure 87 are exclusive resort islands.

2 DIFFICULTY

Logical Steps

The balls below have been rearranged. Can you work out what the new sequence of the balls should be from the clues given below?

- Neither the triangle nor the X is next to the square.
- The circle is only next to one other ball, and it isn't the X.
- The star is two balls to the left of the X.

The first (and only) painting Van Gogh sold in his lifetime was entitled *Red Vineyard at Arles*. It was exhibited in Brussels in 1890 and sold for 400 francs. It now hangs in the Puskin Museum, Moscow.

3

DIFFICULTY

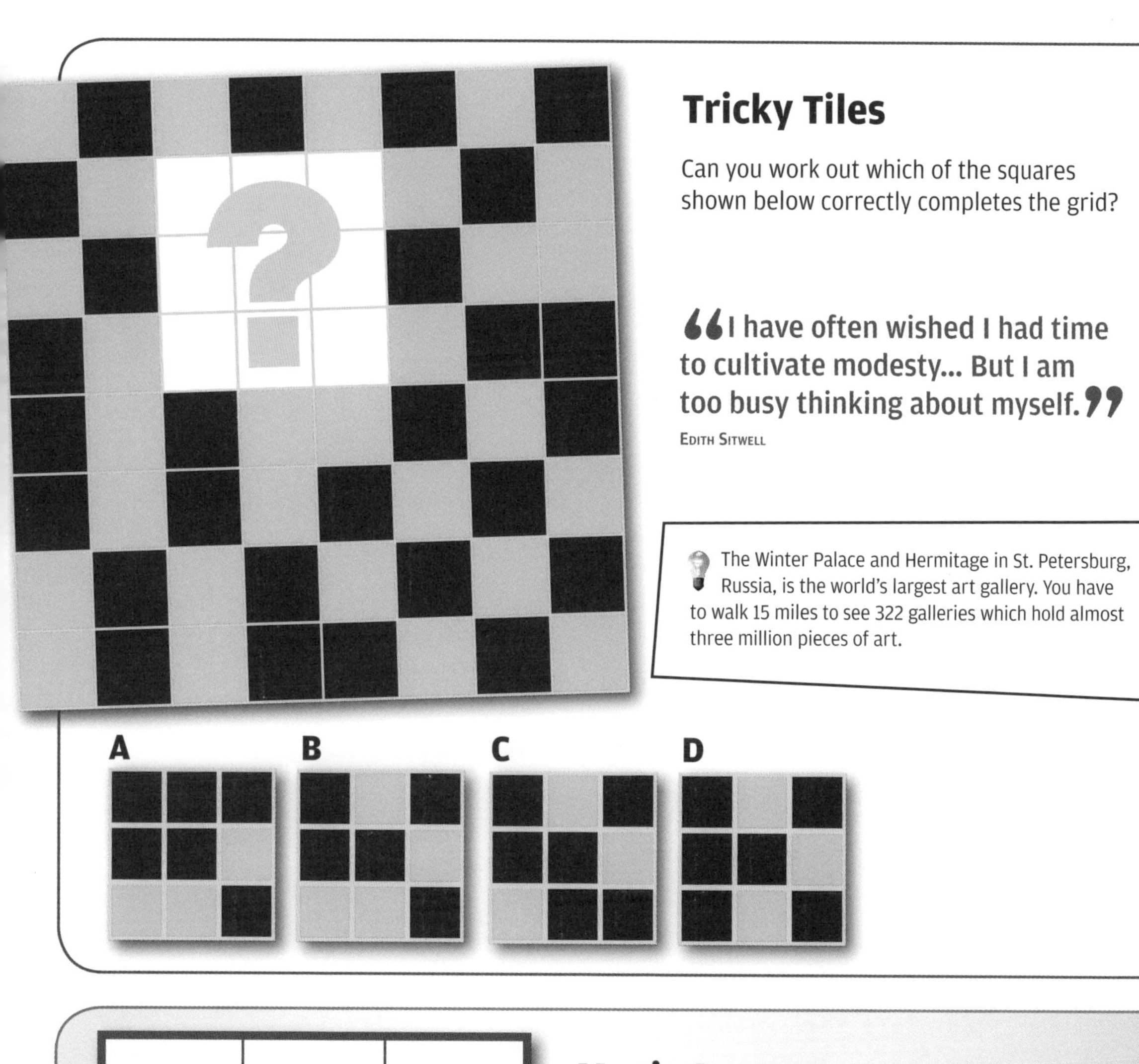

Tricky Tiles

Can you work out which of the squares shown below correctly completes the grid?

“I have often wished I had time to cultivate modesty... But I am too busy thinking about myself.”
EDITH SITWELL

The Winter Palace and Hermitage in St. Petersburg, Russia, is the world’s largest art gallery. You have to walk 15 miles to see 322 galleries which hold almost three million pieces of art.

A B C D

4

DIFFICULTY

8	1	6

Magic Squares

Complete the square using nine consecutive numbers, so that all rows, columns and large diagonals add up to the same total.

“Magic is believing in yourself; if you can do that, you can make anything happen.” JOHANN WOLFGANG VON GOETHE

With 700 native languages, Papua New Guinea is the world’s most linguistically diverse country.

5

DIFFICULTY ☆★★

Carpet Caper

Charlie is trying to describe on the telephone a rug that he would like to buy. What percentage of this rug is blue, what percentage green and what cream?

"The toughest thing about success is that you've got to keep on being a success."

IRVING BERLIN

6

DIFFICULTY ☆★★

Crack the Colour Code

Can you crack the colour code and make your way from one yellow square to the other, moving one square at a time? The blue arrow tells you which way is up...

UP

"To love abundantly is to live abundantly, and to love forever is to live forever."

HENRY DRUMMOND

In ancient Babylon, the bride's father would supply his son-in-law with all the mead (fermented honey beverage) he could drink for a month after the wedding. Because their calendar was lunar or moon-based, this period of free mead was called the 'honey month', or what we now call the 'honeymoon'.

7

DIFFICULTY

Checkers

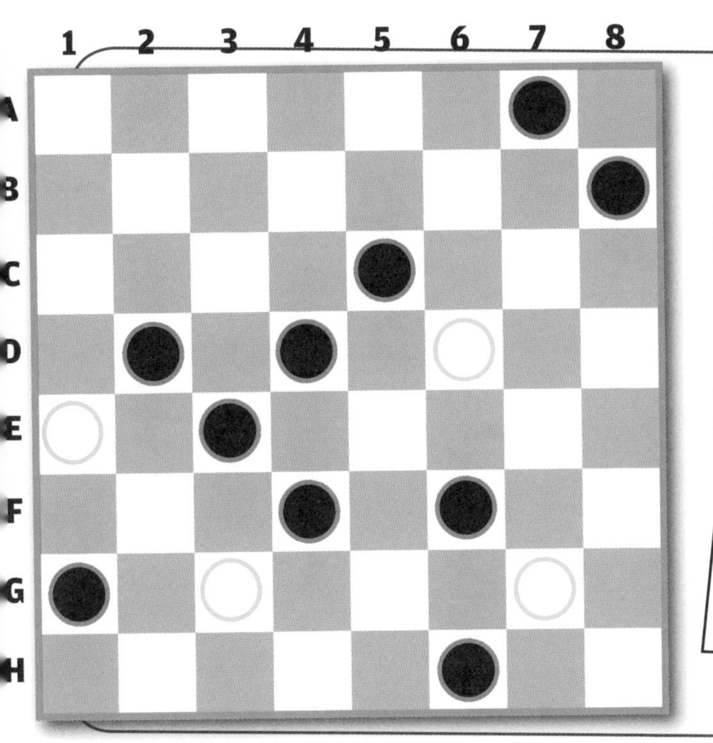

Make a move for white so that eight black pieces are left, none of which are in the same column or row.

“Despise the enemy strategically, but take him seriously tactically.”

MAO TSE-TUNG

From 1788 to 1820, performances of *King Lear* were prohibited on the English stage at the order of reigning monarch, King George III.

8

DIFFICULTY

Bird’s-eye View

Which of the pictures below represents the correct overhead view of this scene?

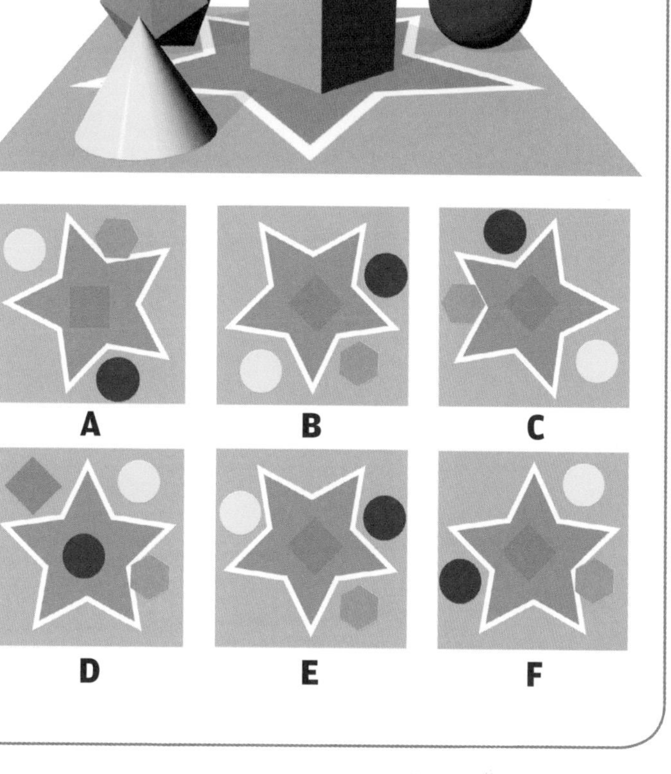

“I seem to have been everywhere in the last 30 years, maybe not in the epicentre but flying around the periphery of extraordinary events and equally extraordinary people.” RUPERT EVERETT

A law was enacted in 1324 that all whales, dolphins and porpoises found in English waters belonged to the monarchy and were to be known as ‘Fishes Royal’. The Natural History Museum has been responsible for investigating all strandings since 1913.

Balancing Act

The arms of these scales are divided into sections – a weight two sections away from the middle will be twice as heavy as a weight one section away. Can you arrange the supplied weights in such a way as to balance the whole scale?

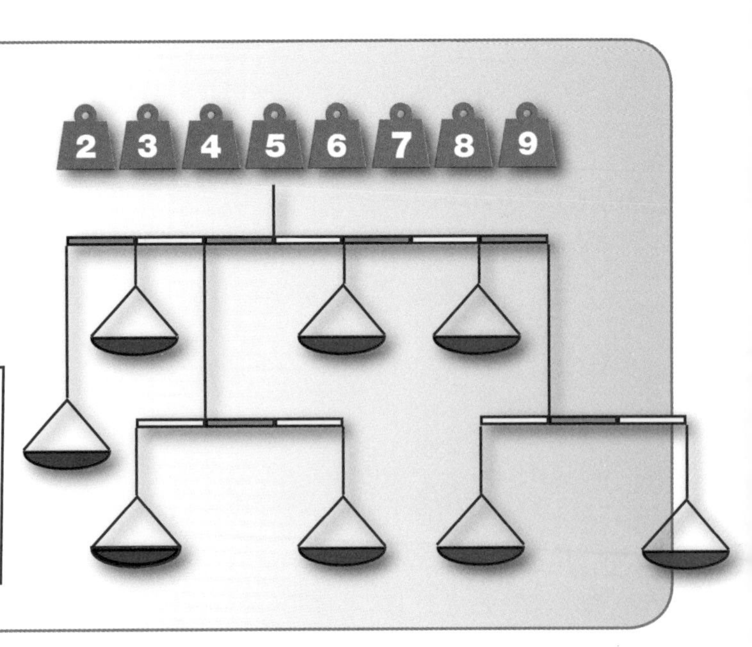

Elizabethan nautical explorers used the astrolabe, the instrument invented by the Greeks, to calculate latitudes through observation of the height of the sun over the horizon.

Complete the Set

Victoria has been decorating sets of boxes to give to her friends as presents, but her naughty son Archie has mixed them up. Can you help her by working out which of the four boxed figures completes the set?

"Everybody knows how to raise children, except the people who have them."

P. J. O'Rourke

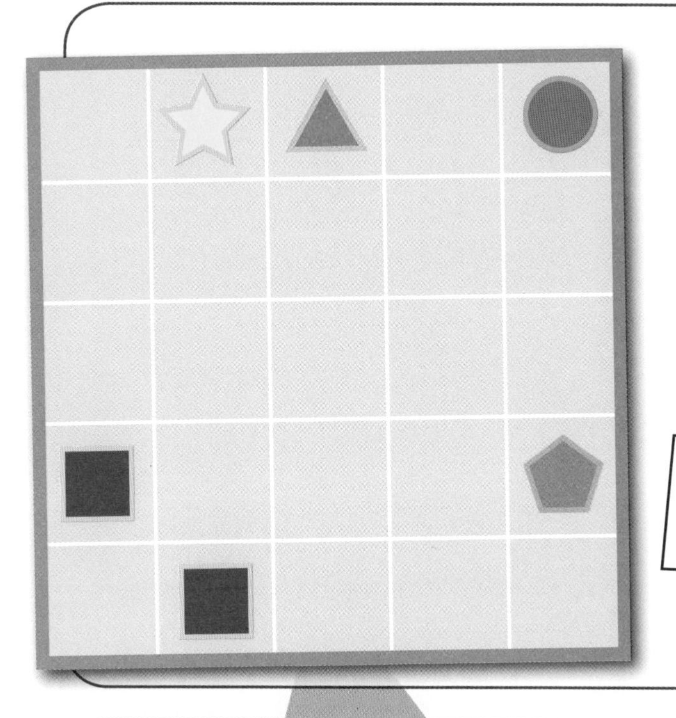

11

DIFFICULTY ★

Mind Align

Fill in the empty squares so that each row, column and long diagonal contains five different symbols.

"If I could read it, I could play it." NAT KING COLE

English physicist and chemist Henry Cavendish not only discovered hydrogen but also determined the mass of the earth.

12

DIFFICULTY ★

Shape Shuffle

Fill up the shuffle box so that each row, column and long diagonal contains four different shapes and the letters A, B, C and D.

A			B
C			
		B	

"A man may be so much of everything that he is nothing of anything."

SAMUEL JOHNSON

In 1956, the Boston Symphony became the first US orchestra to perform in the Soviet Union. In February 2008, the New York Philharmonic is scheduled to do the same in North Korea.

13

DIFFICULTY

Sudoku Sixpack

Fill up the grid so that every row, column and long diagonal contains all the numbers 1, 2, 3, 4, 5 and 6.

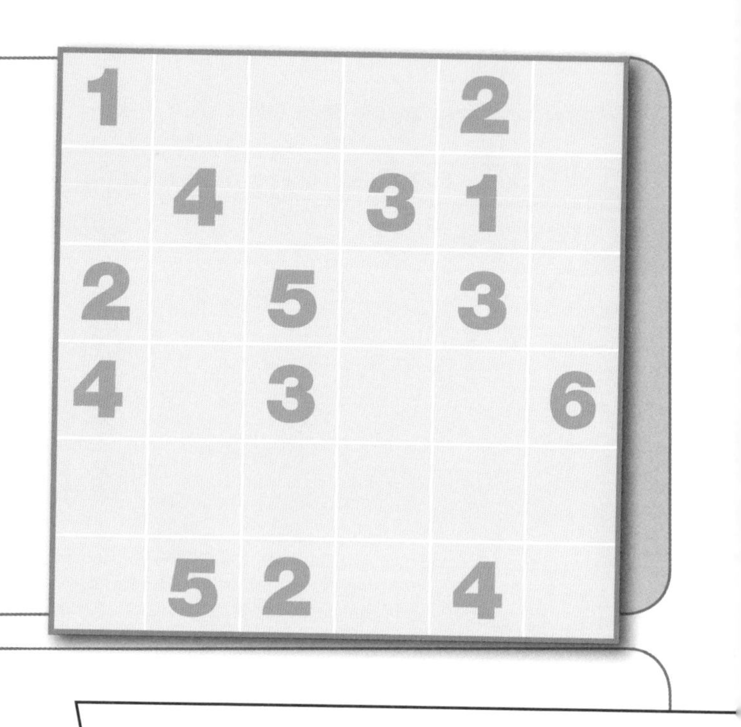

1				2	
	4		3	1	
2		5		3	
4		3			6
	5	2		4	

"What really matters is what you do with what you have." H. G. Wells

14

DIFFICULTY

Snookered!

You're playing stripes in a game of pool, and you've cleaned up all your balls. You're snookered on the black though... Can you spot the shot without hitting any other balls?

The first coin-operated billiard table was patented in 1903. A game on the first pay-for-play table cost one penny.

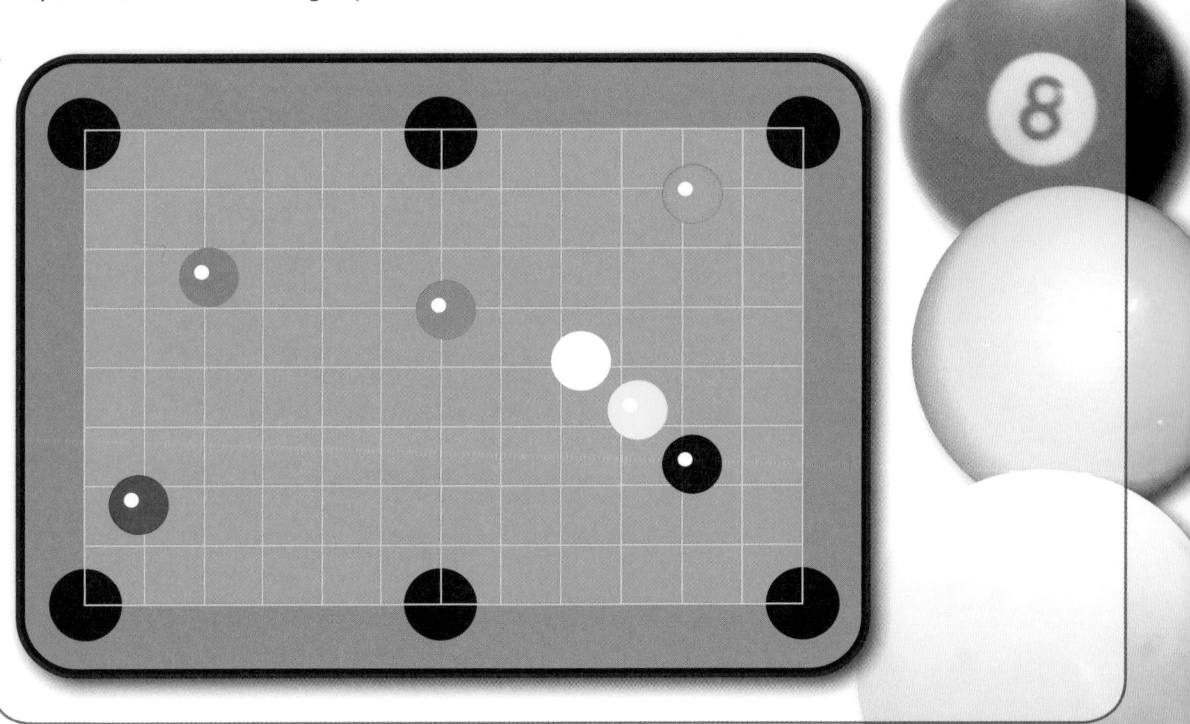

DIFFICULTY ★★★

Molecular Mix Up

Claude the scientist has got a little confused; which of the molecular shapes is not the same as the others?

"When a distinguished but elderly scientist states that something is possible, he is almost certainly right. When he states that something is impossible, he is very probably wrong." Arthur C. Clarke

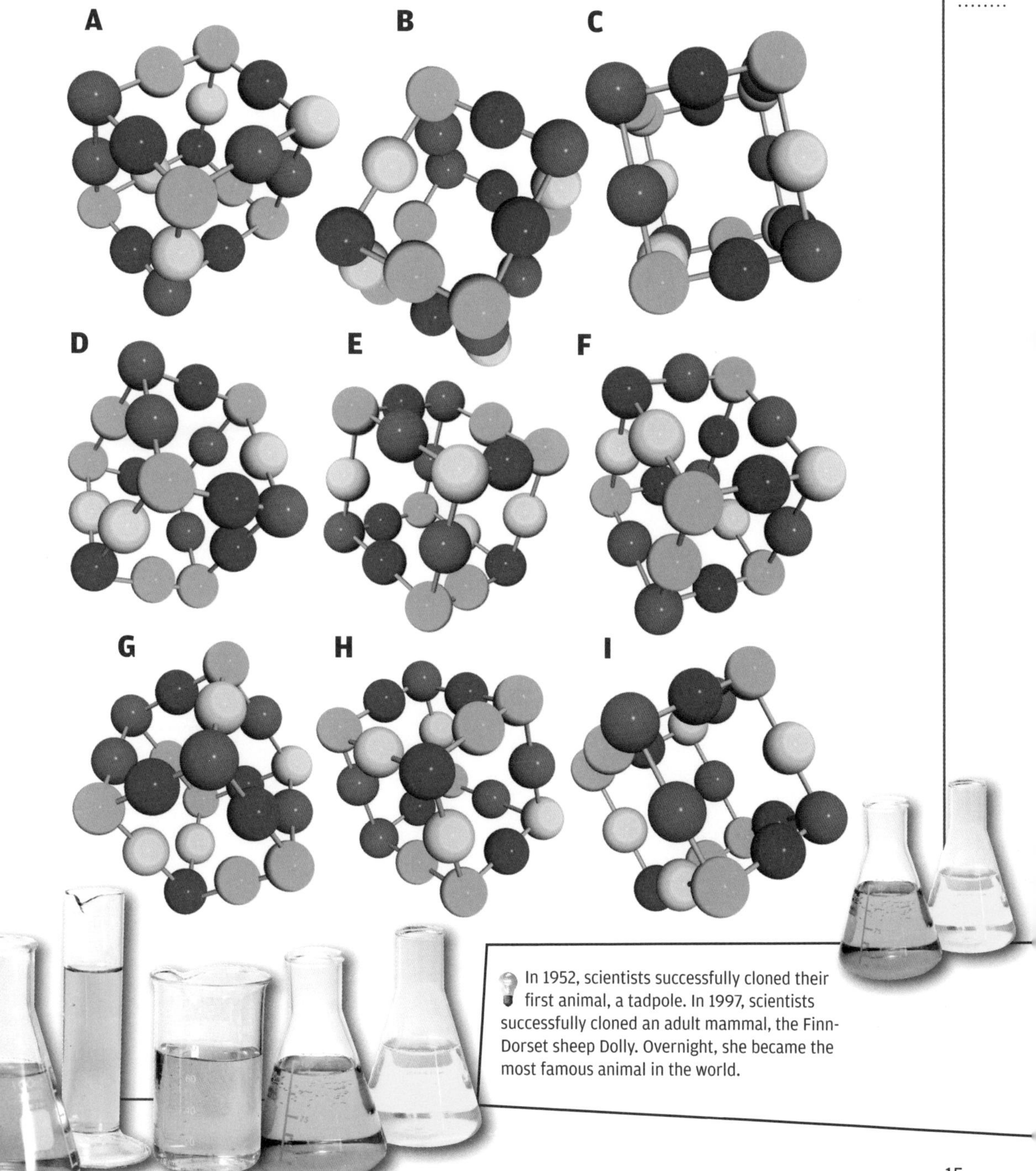

In 1952, scientists successfully cloned their first animal, a tadpole. In 1997, scientists successfully cloned an adult mammal, the Finn-Dorset sheep Dolly. Overnight, she became the most famous animal in the world.

16

DIFFICULTY

Secret Number Sweep

Colour in the squares until all the numbers are surrounded by the correct number of shaded squares. When the puzzles is correctly solved the shaded squares will reveal a number!

0		3		5		5		4		1	
	3		7		5		7		5		1
2		7		5		4		7		4	
	4		4		1		4		8		3
1		3		2		4		7		4	
	0		0		3		7		7		2
0		0		2		4		7		5	
	3		1		2		5		8		4
3		4		2		1		5		8	
	7		6		4		5		8		4
3		6		7		6		7		4	
1	2		4		5		5	4	4		1

"Everywhere is within walking distance if you have the time."

STEVEN WRIGHT

The month of May is named after Maia – the Greek Goddess of Growth.

17

Loop Link

Connect adjacent dots with either horizontal or vertical lines to create a continuous unbroken loop which never crosses over itself. Some, but not all of the boxes are numbered. The numbers in these boxes tell you how many sides of that box are used by your unbroken line.

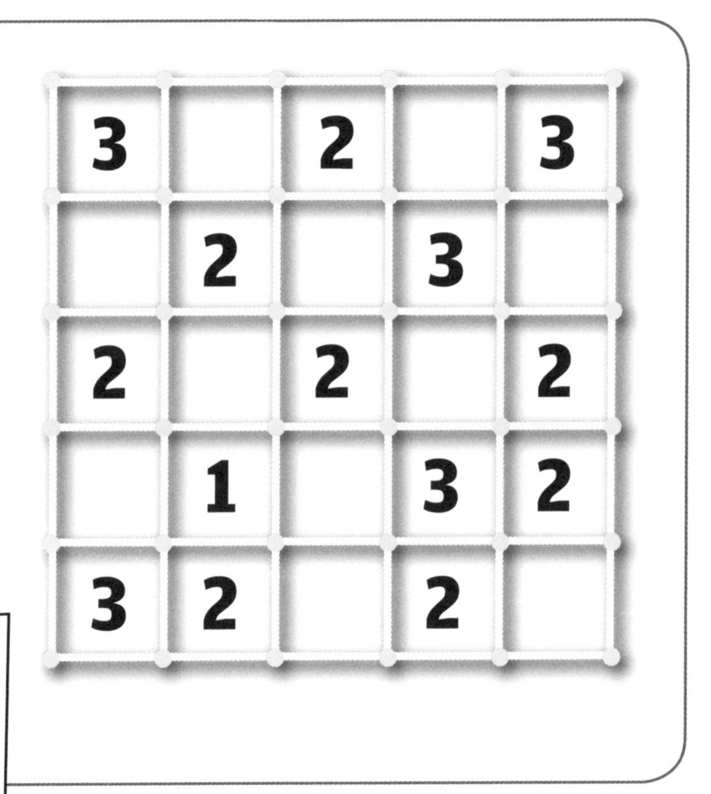

"Life is just one damned thing after another."

ELBERT HUBBARD

The longest unambiguously documented lifespan is that of Jeanne Calment of France (1875-1997), who was aged 122 years. She met Vincent Van Gogh when aged 14.

The top three beef-exporting countries are Brazil, Australia and Argentina. Brazil is also the world's largest poultry exporter.

18

DIFFICULTY ★★★

Corner Conundrum

Use the numbers in the red corners to make the central number the same way in all three cases. What number should replace the question mark?

19

DIFFICULTY ☆☆★

On the Radar

The numbers in some cells in the grid indicate the exact number of black cells that should border it. Shade these black, until all the numbers are surrounded by the correct number of black cells.

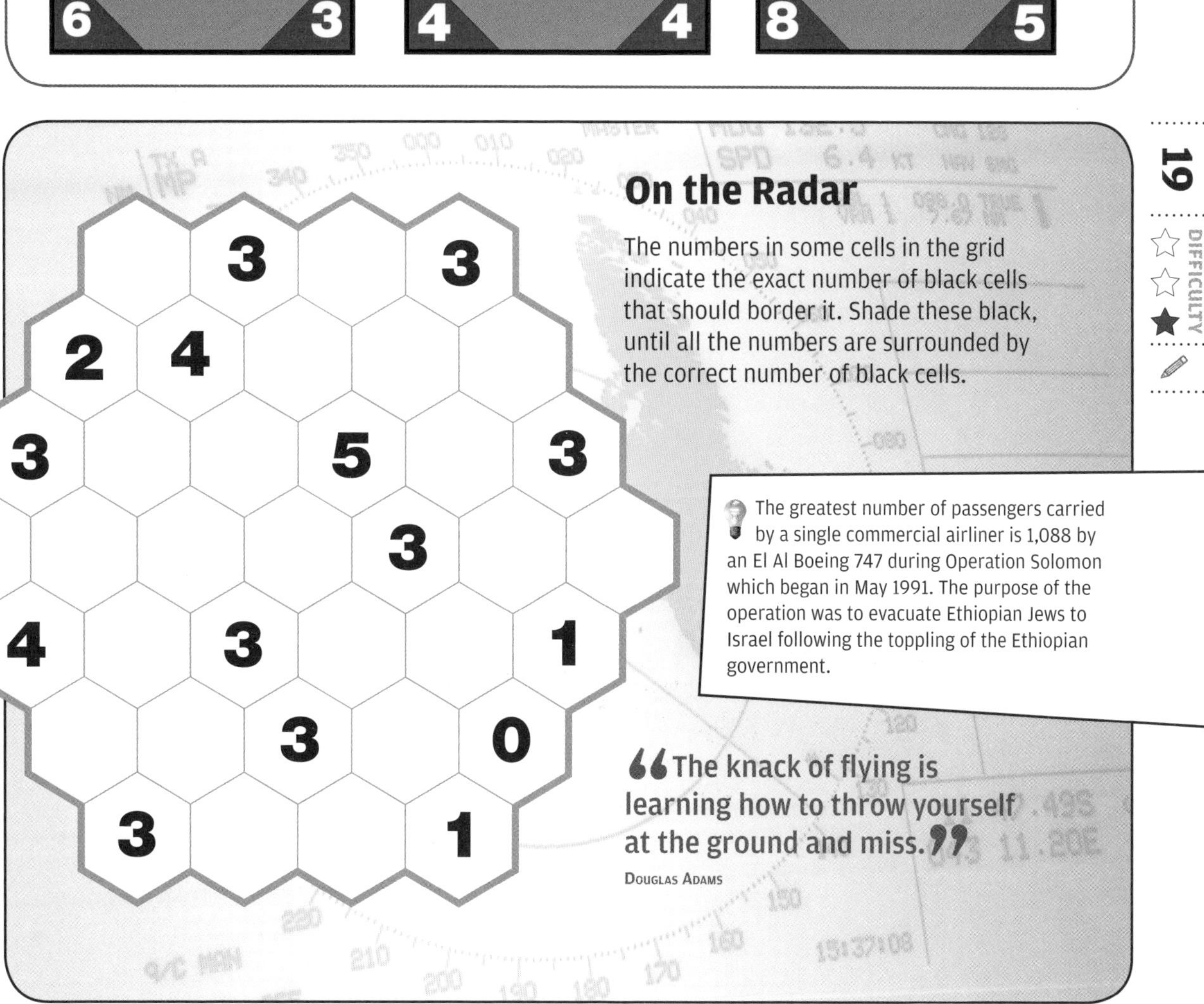

The greatest number of passengers carried by a single commercial airliner is 1,088 by an El Al Boeing 747 during Operation Solomon which began in May 1991. The purpose of the operation was to evacuate Ethiopian Jews to Israel following the toppling of the Ethiopian government.

"The knack of flying is learning how to throw yourself at the ground and miss."

Douglas Adams

Ride Out!

After the bank robbery, Tex, Six-Gun and Hoss split up and headed for their hideouts. Can you name each bandit, the horse he rode, and where he escaped to?

- Hoss rode Blanco to a town ending in the letter 'O'.
- Six-Gun MacGee didn't ride Sunset, or to Dodge.
- Williams, who wasn't called Tex, didn't ride to Reno.

Rodeos, a popular wild west pastime to test a cowboy's skills, are the only national spectator sport to originate entirely in the United States. A typical rodeo includes a variety of events from calf roping and steer wrestling to saddle-bronc and bull riding.

	Deluth	Williams	MacGee	Bullet	Sunset	Blanco	Reno	Dodge	Chicago
Tex									
Six-Gun									
Hoss									
Reno									
Dodge									
Chicago									
Bullet									
Sunset									
Blanco									

“A lot of old guys in movies are like cowboys – they talk like cowboys and they dress like cowboys.” Val Kilmer

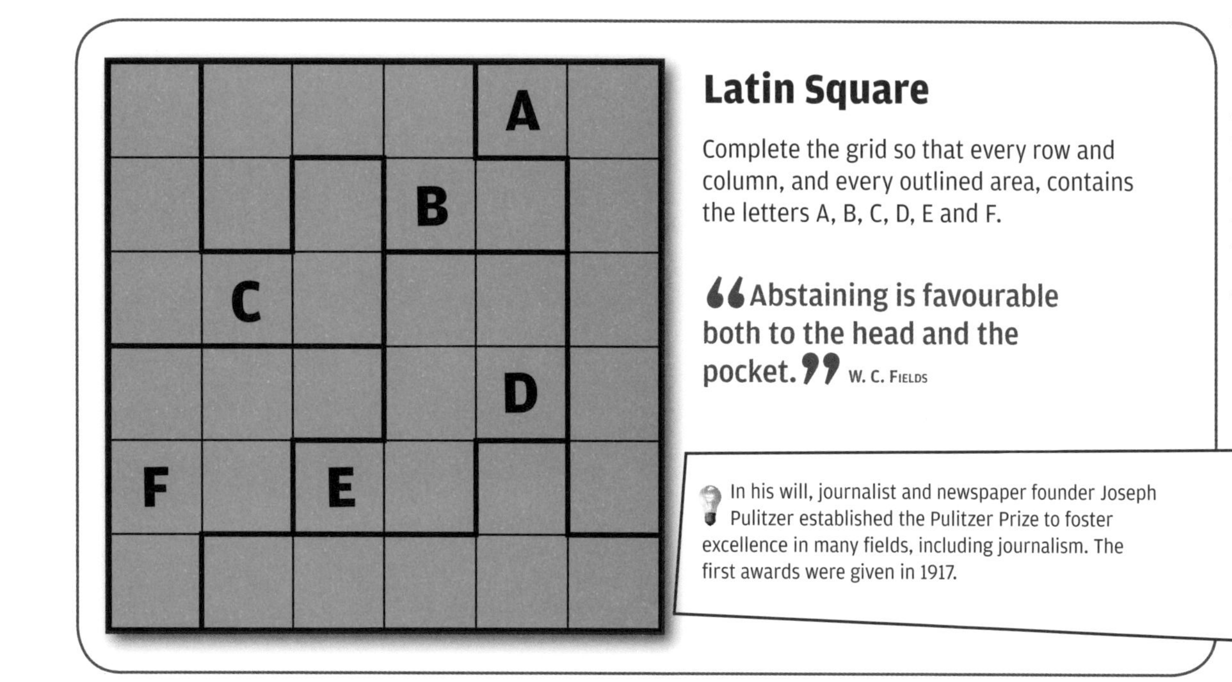

21

DIFFICULTY

Latin Square

Complete the grid so that every row and column, and every outlined area, contains the letters A, B, C, D, E and F.

“Abstaining is favourable both to the head and the pocket.” W. C. Fields

In his will, journalist and newspaper founder Joseph Pulitzer established the Pulitzer Prize to foster excellence in many fields, including journalism. The first awards were given in 1917.

22

DIFFICULTY

Sum People

23

?

31

10

21 15 24 22

Each of the different pictures in the box represents a number. The numbers at the end of each row and the bottom of each column are the totals of the numbers in that row or column added together. Can you work out which number each picture represents and so work out what the question mark should be?

In winning the US Masters at Augusta in 1997, Tiger Woods smashed a number of records. He was the youngest ever player to win the championship. He won by 12 stokes – the greatest ever margin of victory – and his final four round score of 270, 18 under par, was an Augusta record. He was also the first black player to win a major golf tournament.

Matching Pair

Only one of the tiles below is unique, the other 14 all have an exact double. Can you find the one-off?

Some of the earliest examples of mosaic patterns on glazed tiles uncovered came from the columns of the temple at Ubaid in Mesopotamia, and are attributed to the second half of the 2nd millennium B.C.

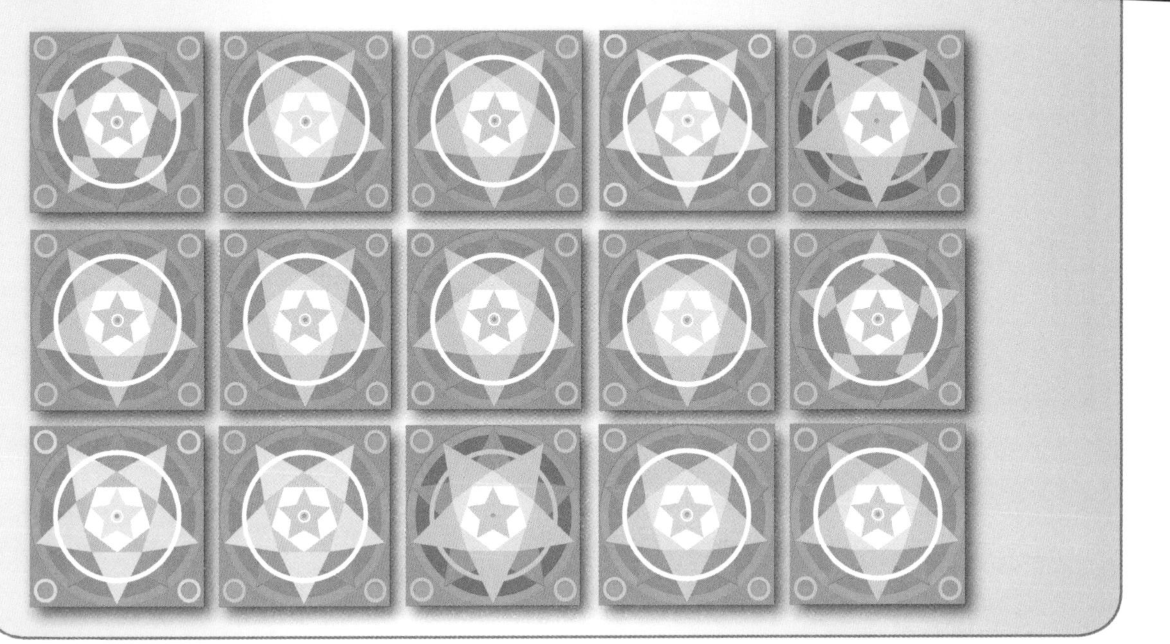

More or Less

The arrows indicate whether a number in a box is greater or smaller than an adjacent number. Complete the grid so that all rows and columns contain the numbers 1 to 5.

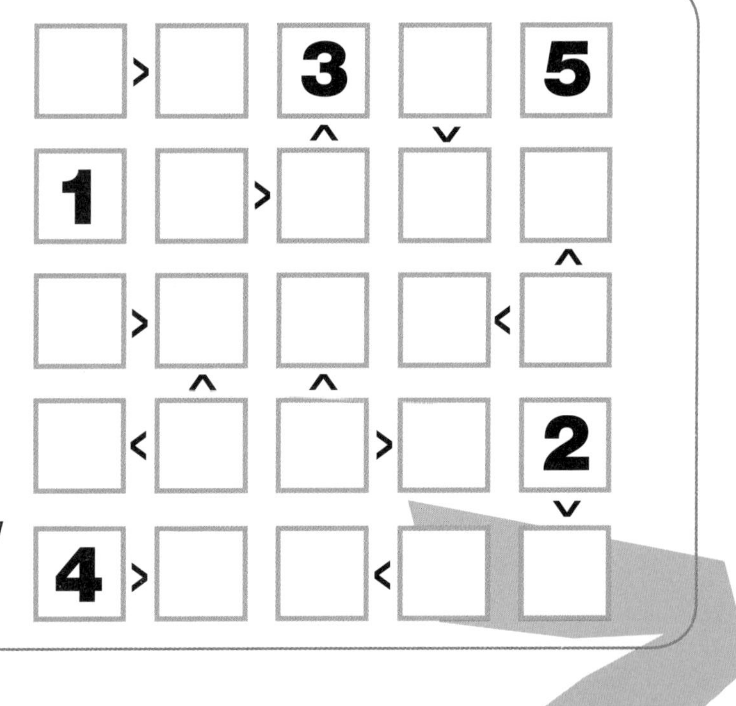

“Even a rich man thinks he has to go down to the office every day. Not because he likes it but because he can't think of anything else to do.”

W. H. Auden

The philosopher and writer Jean Paul Sartre declined the Nobel Prize he was awarded in 1964 citing as his reason his consistent refusal to accept any awards.

The annual survey by car paint manufacturer DuPont found that in 2007, white, by a brief margin, had overtaken silver as the most popular car colour in the United States.

Swatch Switch

One of our swatches is missing! Can you work out the four colour sequence that completes the set?

Fair's Square

The numbers by each row and column describe black squares and groups of black squares that are adjoining in that row or column. Colour in all the black squares and a six number combination will be revealed.

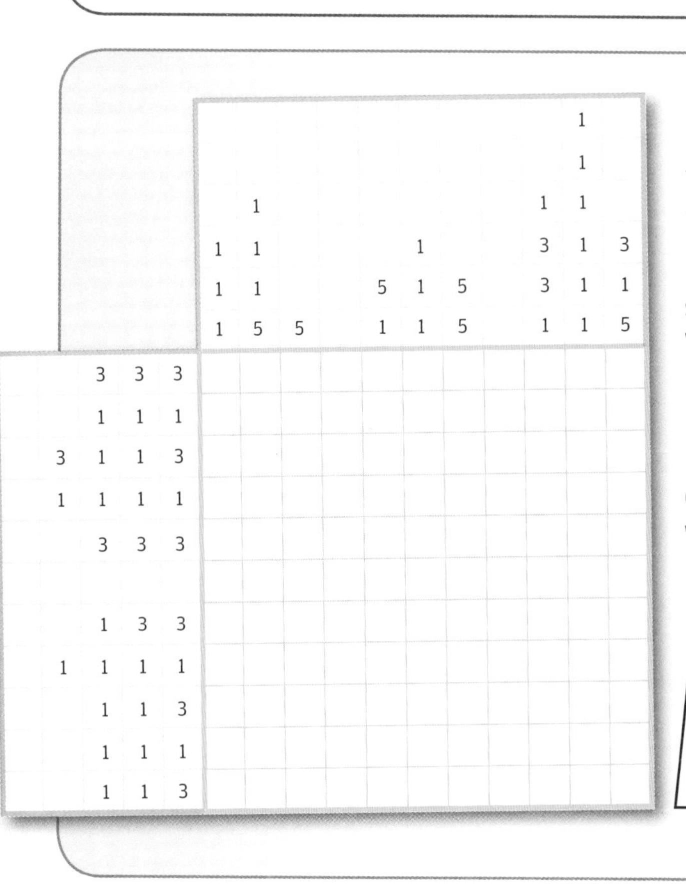

❝Most of the time I don't have much fun. The rest of the time I don't have any fun at all.❞

Woody Allen

The world's smallest city block is in Dothan, Alabama, at the intersection of North Appletree, Museum and Troy Street. The tiny land triangle features a stop sign, a yield sign, a street sign, and a granite marker placed in 1964, stating that it is the world's smallest city block.

Minesweeper

The numbers in some squares in the grid indicate the exact number of black squares that should surround it. Shade these squares until all the numbers are surrounded by the correct number of black squares.

“It's discouraging to think how many people are shocked by honesty and how few by deceit.” NOEL COWARD

2			1		2		
		3	3		3	3	
2	3		3		3		2
		4	4	3		2	
3			3		3		1
3				2		2	1
	5		3	2			2
2		2	2		2		

28
DIFFICULTY

Odd Number Out

All these numbers appear twice in the box except one. Can you spot the singleton?

“A few honest men are better than numbers.” OLIVER CROMWELL

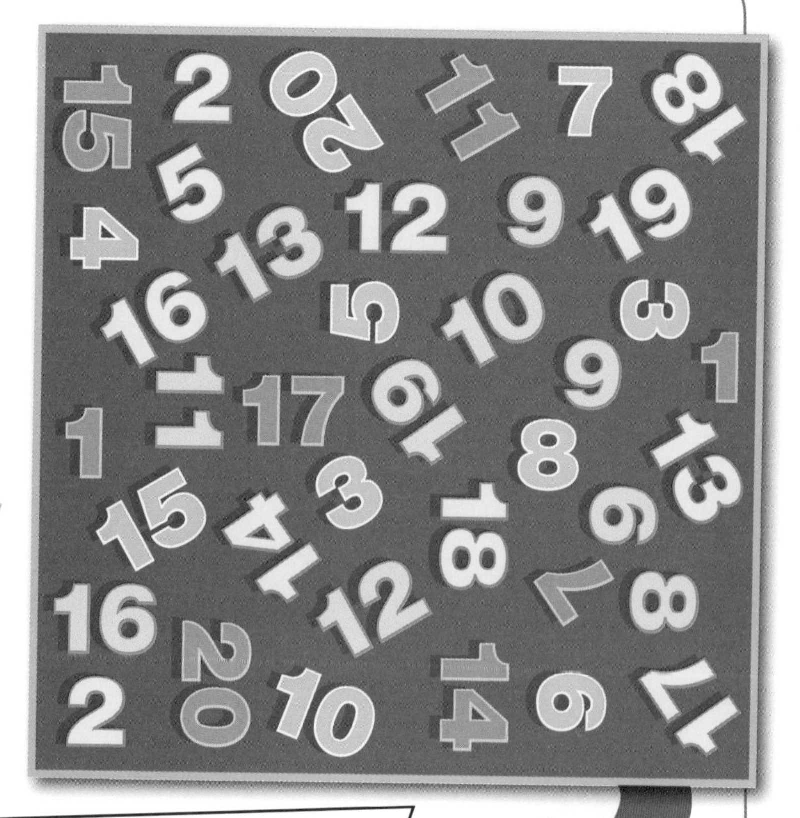

In July 2006, Polish President Lech Kaczynski swore in his country's new Prime Minister - his identical twin brother Jaroslaw.

29

DIFFICULTY ★★★

The South China tiger is believed to be the antecedent of all known species of the big cat.

In the Middle

What numbers should appear in the hubs of these number wheels?

30

DIFFICULTY ★★★

		6		7		5	3	
8			1	3		2		
					2			
9				5			4	
		4			6		8	5
2	8		7	9		6		
	1			6				9
	7					4	2	1
5			4				6	

Sudoku

Complete the grid so that all rows and columns, and each outlined block of nine squares, contain the numbers 1, 2, 3, 4, 5, 6, 7, 8 and 9.

“Have the courage to be ignorant of a great number of things, in order to avoid the calamity of being ignorant of everything.” SYDNEY SMITH

Sudoku is so popular in Japan that sudoku magazines sell over 600,000 copies each month.

Where's the Pair?

Only two of the shapes below match exactly - can you find them?

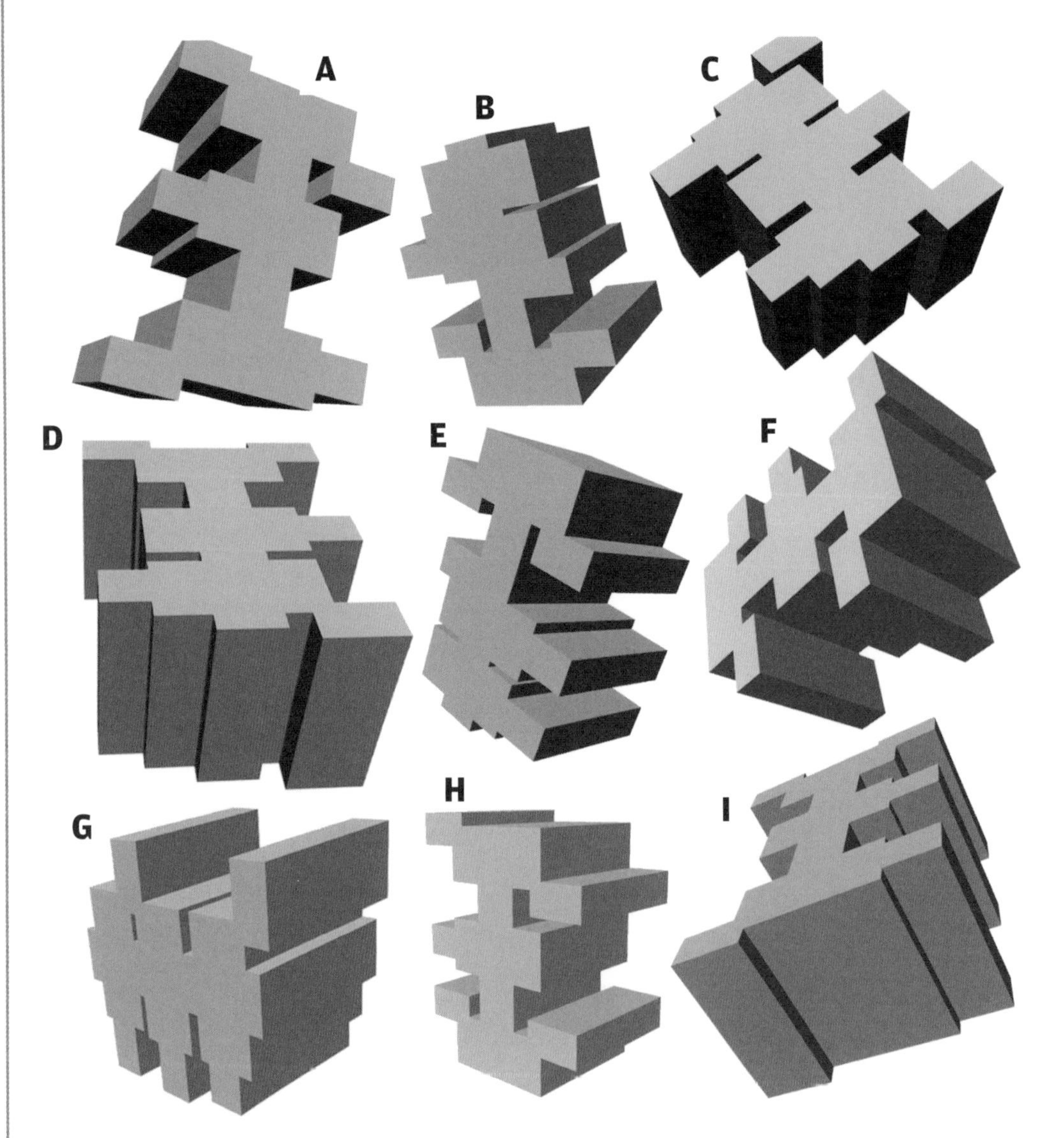

The flower with the world's largest bloom is the *Rafflesia arnoldii*. Found in the rainforests of Indonesia, it can grow to be three feet across and weigh up to 15 pounds. When in bloom it emits a repulsive smell, like rotting meat, which attracts the insects that pollinate the plant.

"I am very interested in the universe - I am specialising in the universe and all that surrounds it." PETER COOK

32

DIFFICULTY

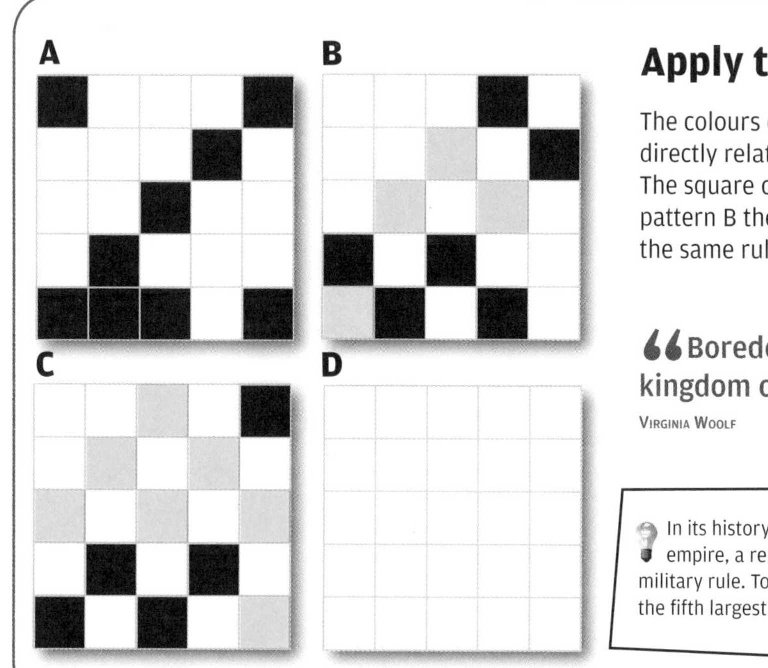

Apply the Rules

The colours of each square in pattern B are directly related to the colours in pattern A. The square colours in pattern C relate to pattern B the same way. Can you apply the same rules and fill in pattern D?

"Boredom is the legitimate kingdom of the philanthropic."

VIRGINIA WOOLF

In its history Brazil has been a colony, an empire, a republic and has been under military rule. Today it is a democracy and the fifth largest nation on earth.

33

DIFFICULTY

Make the Cut

Cut two straight lines through this shape to create three shapes that are identical.

"You do not merely want to be considered just the best of the best. You want to be considered the only ones who do what you do."

JERRY GARCIA

Caligula, Roman emperor from 12-41 AD famously appointed his horse as a senator.

Next!

In the sequence below, which of the numbered alternatives, A, B, C or D, should replace the question mark?

In 1912, Alfred Wegener proposed the theory of Continental Drift - the idea that one super-continent consisting of what we know today as Africa and South America had existed millions of years ago. He called it Pangaea.

A B C D

Make it Out

Which of the coloured-in bucket and spade images matches the silhouette?

A B C D E F G H

"Every man who possibly can should force himself to a holiday of a full month in a year, whether he feels like taking it or not." William James

Praia do Cassino, Brazil, is commonly known as the longest beach in the world. Estimated at 254 kilometres long, it stretches from the entrance to the Rio Grande seaport to nearly Chuí, on the border with Uruguay.

36

DIFFICULTY ☆★★

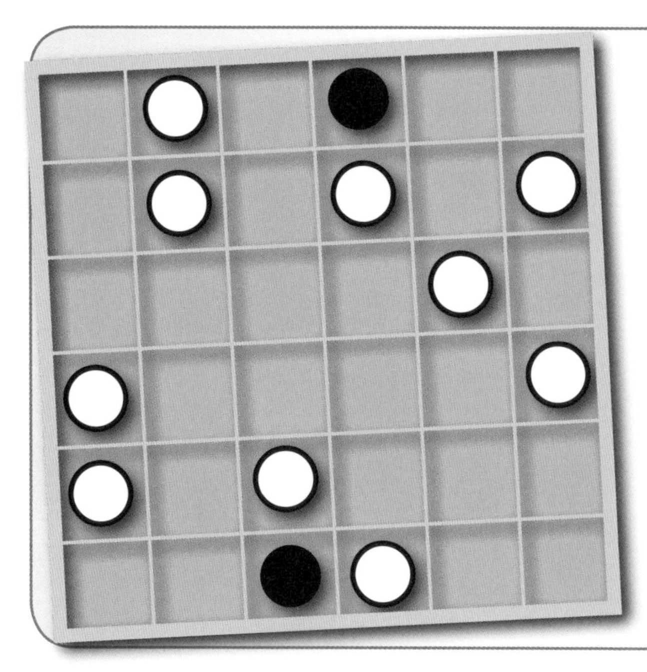

Round in Circles

Draw a single continuous line that passes through all the circles. The line must enter and leave each box in the centre of one of its four sides.

Black Circle Turn left or right in the box, and the line must pass straight through the next and previous boxes.
White Circle Travel straight through the box, and the line must turn in the next and/or previous box.

“Attitude is a little thing that makes a big difference.”
Winston Churchill

37

DIFFICULTY ☆★★

Jiggery Pokery

Which of the four pieces below can complete the jigsaw and make a perfect square?

“Success is a science; if you have the conditions, you get the result.” Oscar Wilde

A B C D

E F G H

The state of Idaho most likely got its name as a result of a hoax in the 1860s when lobbyist George M. Willing suggested it when Congress were seeking to name the new territory. He claimed the word originated from Shoshone, a Native American language, and meant 'the sun comes from the mountains'. He later admitted he had made it up, but the name stuck.

38

DIFFICULTY ★

Spot the Slate

Two square slates have been broken into four pieces each. Can you reunite them?

The US Bullion Depository at Fort Knox, Kentucky, opened in January 1937. The building cost $560,000 to construct and the materials included 16,000 cubic feet of granite, 4,200 cubic yards of concrete, 750 tons of reinforcing steel and 670 tons of structural steel.

39

DIFFICULTY ★★

Invisible Blocks

Assuming all blocks that are not visible from this angle are present, how many blocks have been removed from this 6 x 6 x 6 cube?

“Sometimes paranoia’s just having all the facts.”

William Burroughs

In the Middle Ages, fern seeds were thought to be invisible since ferns don’t have seeds. They were also said to grant invisibility as Gadshill from Shakespeare’s *Henry IV* claims “We steal as in a castle, cock-sure. We have the recipe of fern-seed, we walk invisible”.

Can You Cut It?

40

DIFFICULTY

Cut a straight line through this shape to create two shapes that are identical.

"There can't be any crisis next week. My schedule is already full."

HENRY KISSINGER

Previously known as the *Daily Universal Register*, *The Times* was published for the first time on 1 January 1788.

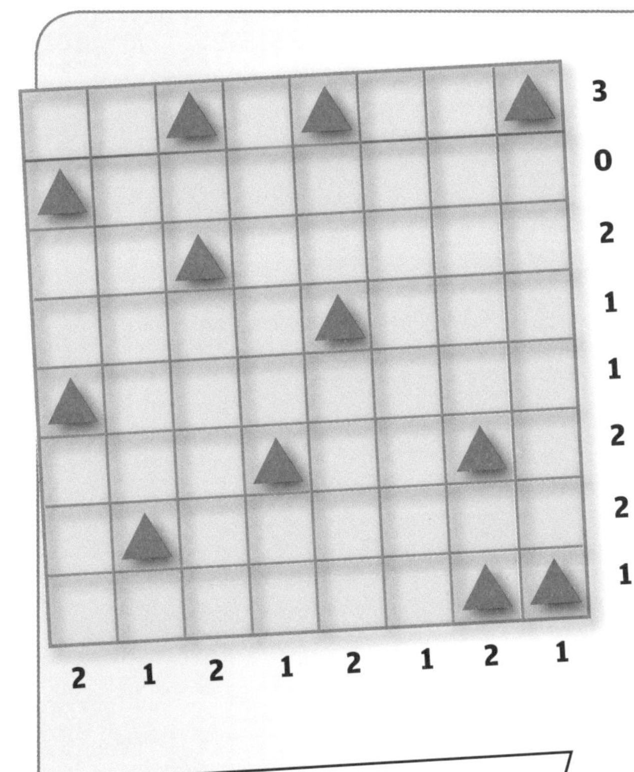

Perfect Pitch

41

DIFFICULTY

In the field on this map, every tree has one tent found horizontally or vertically adjacent to it. No tent can be in an adjacent square to another tent (even diagonally). The numbers by each row and column tell you how many tents are there. Can you locate all the tents?

"One thing that's certain about the great outdoors: when you come back inside you'll be scratching."

P. J. O'ROURKE

TREE

TENT

The world's rarest living creature is the Abingdon Island giant tortoise, which is represented by just one specimen. As there is no hope of discovering a mate, this particular species is now effectively extinct.

Seeing Double

All these shapes appear twice in the box except one. Can you spot the singleton?

“Advertising is the rattling of a stick inside a swill bucket.”

George Orwell

Renaissance polymath Leonardo da Vinci is believed to have invented scissors.

Lucky Number

What's the missing number?

Gambling was legalised in Las Vegas, Nevada, in 1931. The first people to be issued a gambling licence were Mayme V. Stocker and J.H. Morgan, on 20 March 1931. Their three-month licence cost $1,410.

44

DIFFICULTY ★☆☆

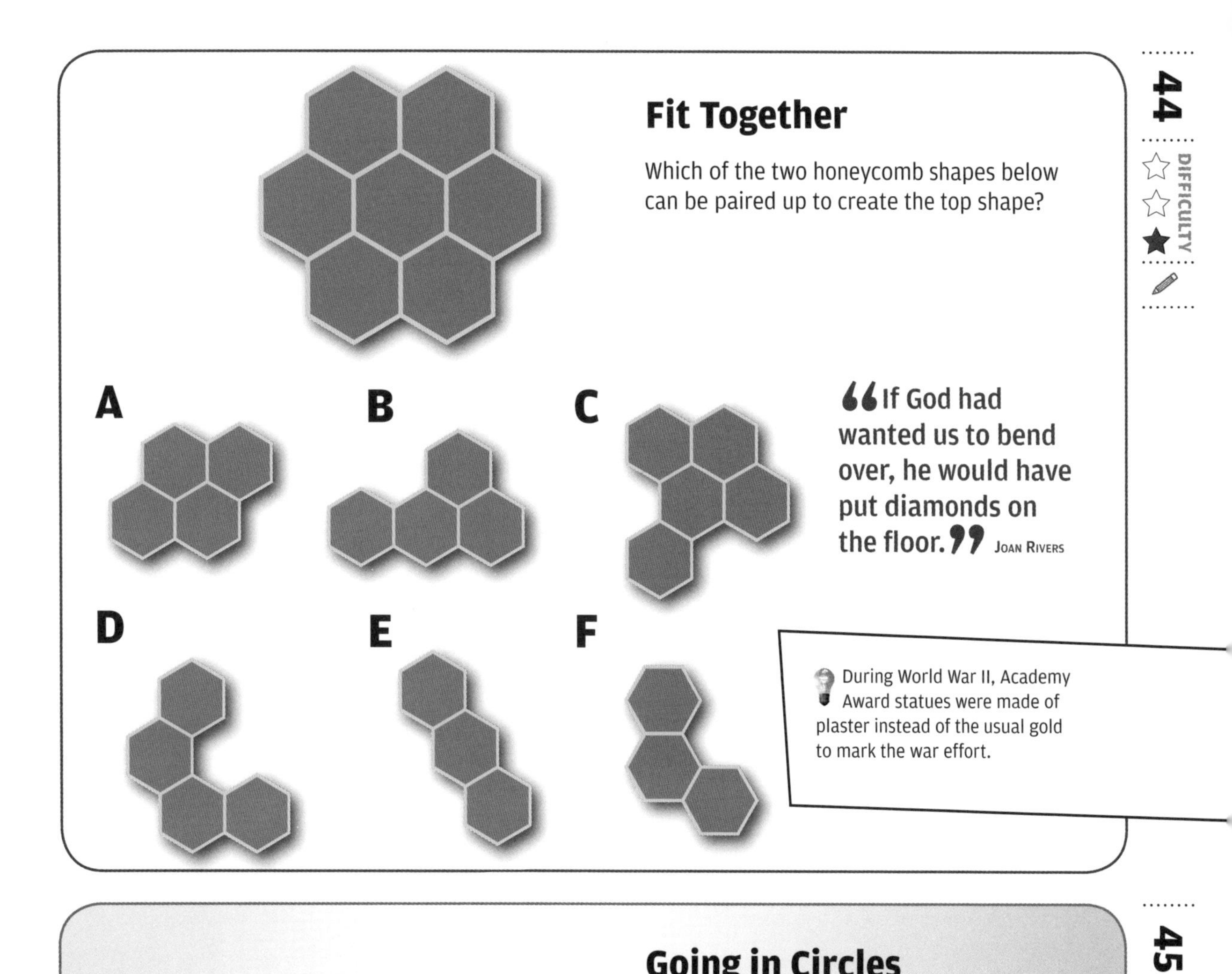

Fit Together

Which of the two honeycomb shapes below can be paired up to create the top shape?

“If God had wanted us to bend over, he would have put diamonds on the floor.” JOAN RIVERS

During World War II, Academy Award statues were made of plaster instead of the usual gold to mark the war effort.

45

DIFFICULTY ★★☆

Going in Circles

Use the corner circles to make the central number the same way in all three cases. What number should replace the question mark?

The rock group Pink Floyd took their name from two blues musicians - Pink Anderson and Floyd Council.

3 2 6 3 3 1

30 54 ?

2 4 5 1 8 2

46

DIFFICULTY ☆★★

Boxing Clever

The value of each shape is the number of sides each shape has, multiplied by the number within it. Thus a square containing the number 4 has a value of 16. Find a block of four squares (two squares wide by two squares high) with a total value of exactly 100.

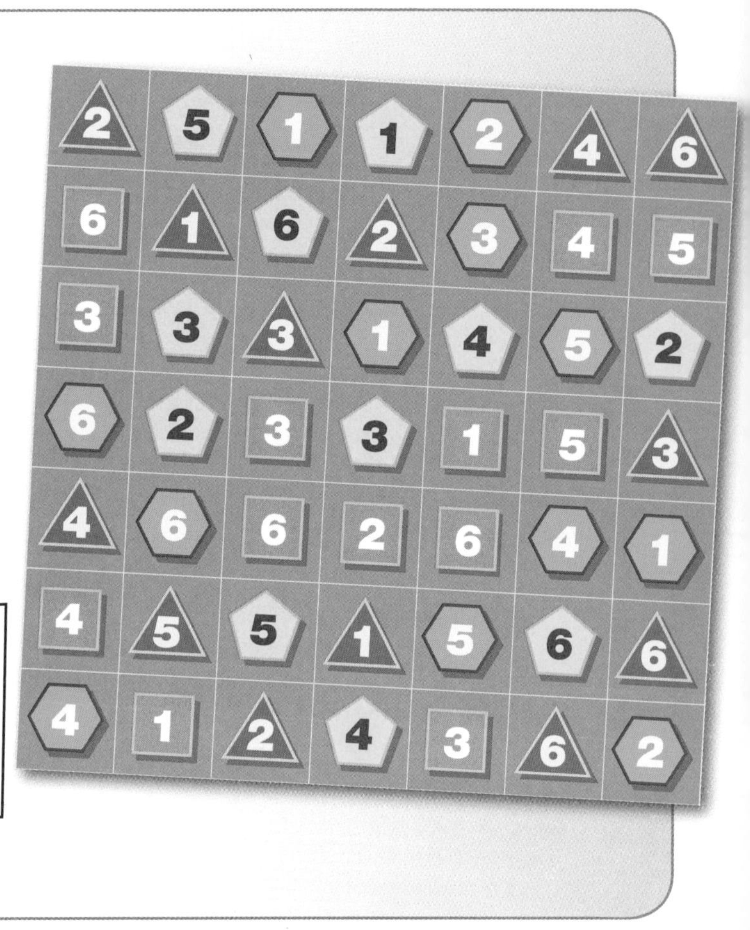

“A lot of fellows nowadays have a B.A., M.D., or a PhD. Unfortunately they don’t have a J.O.B.” Fats Domino

Sir Hans Sloane was a physicist and collector of curiosities in the eighteenth century. Upon his death in 1753 he bequeathed his collection to the nation and it went on to form the basis of the British Museum which opened six years later.

47

DIFFICULTY ☆★★

What’s Coming Next?

The sequence below follows a logical pattern. Can you work out the colour and shape of the next in line?

Sir Hans Sloane was responsible for the invention of milk chocolate. Whilst travelling in Jamaica he found the local drink of cocoa and water much more palatable if mixed with milk.

“Success is having to worry about every damn thing in the world, except money.” Johnny Cash

All at Sea

The numbers on the side and bottom of the grid indicate occupied squares or groups of consecutive occupied squares in each row or column. Can you finish the grid so that it contains four cruisers, three launches and two buoys, and the numbers tally?

"As a general rule, nobody has money who ought to have it."

BENJAMIN DISRAELI

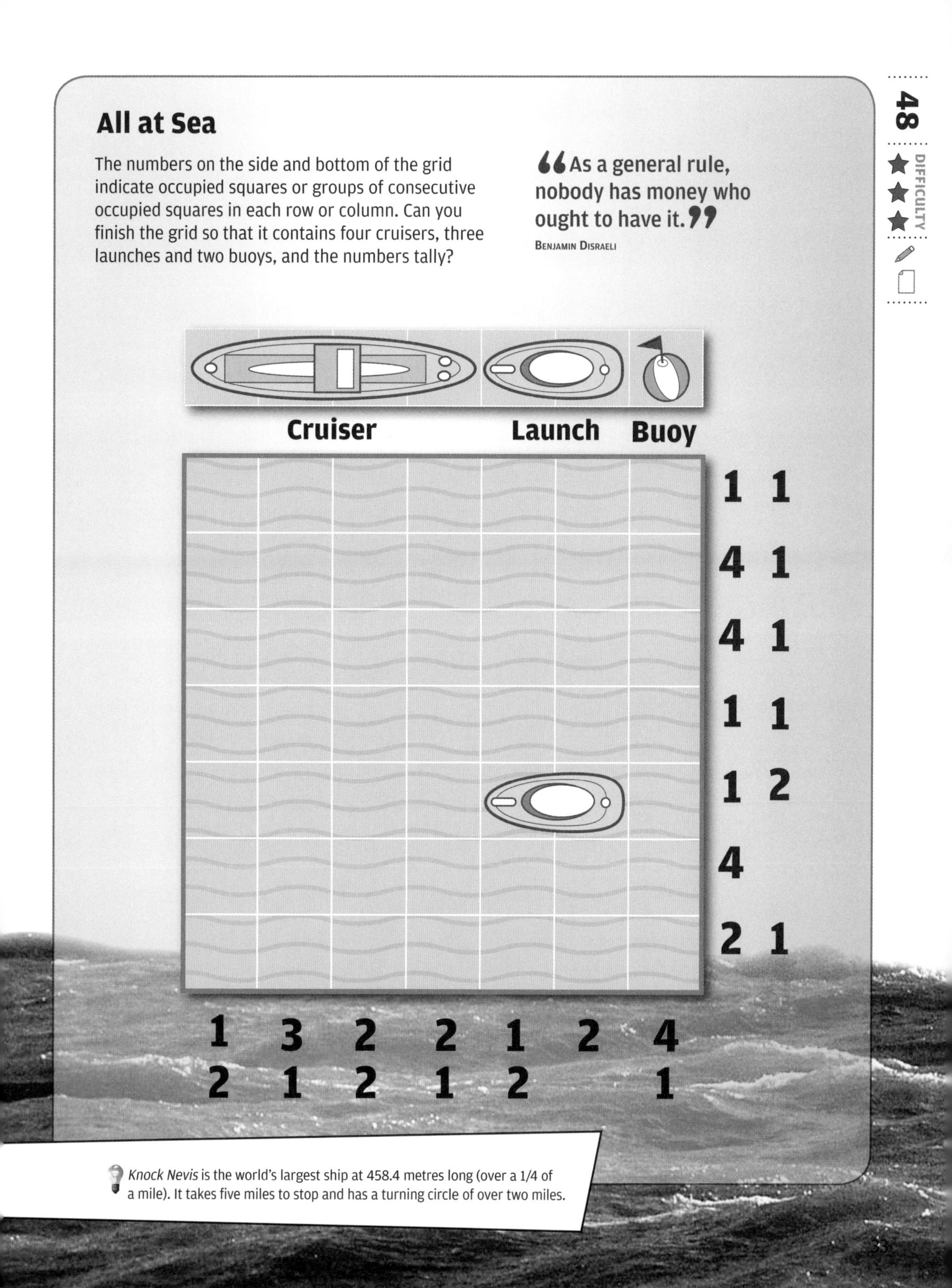

Knock Nevis is the world's largest ship at 458.4 metres long (over a 1/4 of a mile). It takes five miles to stop and has a turning circle of over two miles.

Taking Shape

What shape, in what colour, should replace the question mark so that the grid follows a pattern?

"A man's worth is no greater than his ambitions."

Marcus Aurelius

French writer Voltaire is the man responsible for the theory that a falling apple provided the impetus for Newton's theory of gravity. Voltaire claimed to have been told the story by Newton's niece.

50

DIFFICULTY

Pentagon Puzzler

The numbers on these pentagons follow a pattern. Your task is to uncover the secret to the pattern and fill in the blanks to complete the puzzle.

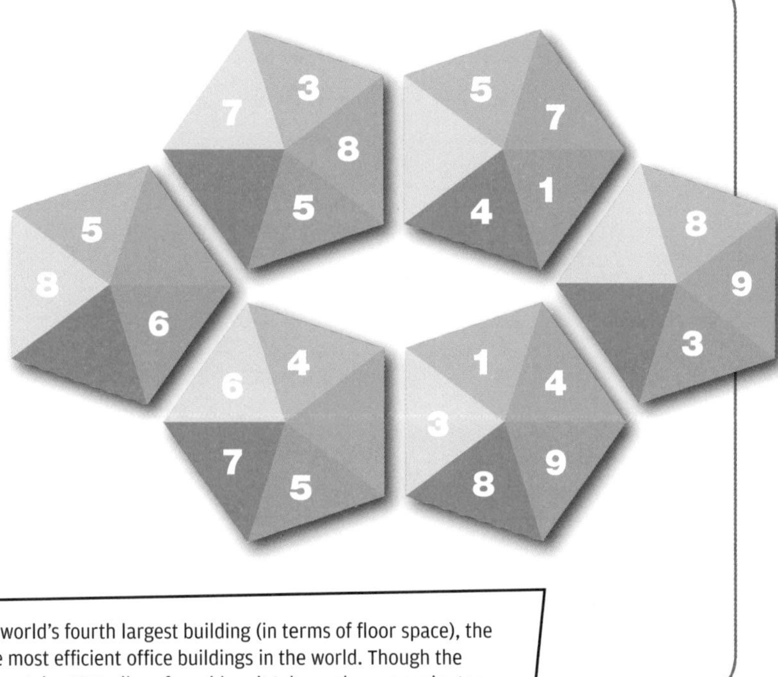

"Dreams are renewable. No matter what our age or condition, there are still untapped possibilities within us and new beauty waiting to be born."

Dale E. Turner

Despite being over 60 years old and the world's fourth largest building (in terms of floor space), the Pentagon is still thought to be one of the most efficient office buildings in the world. Though the giant US Defence HQ at Arlington, Virginia, contains 17.5 miles of corridors it takes only seven minutes to walk between any two points in the building.

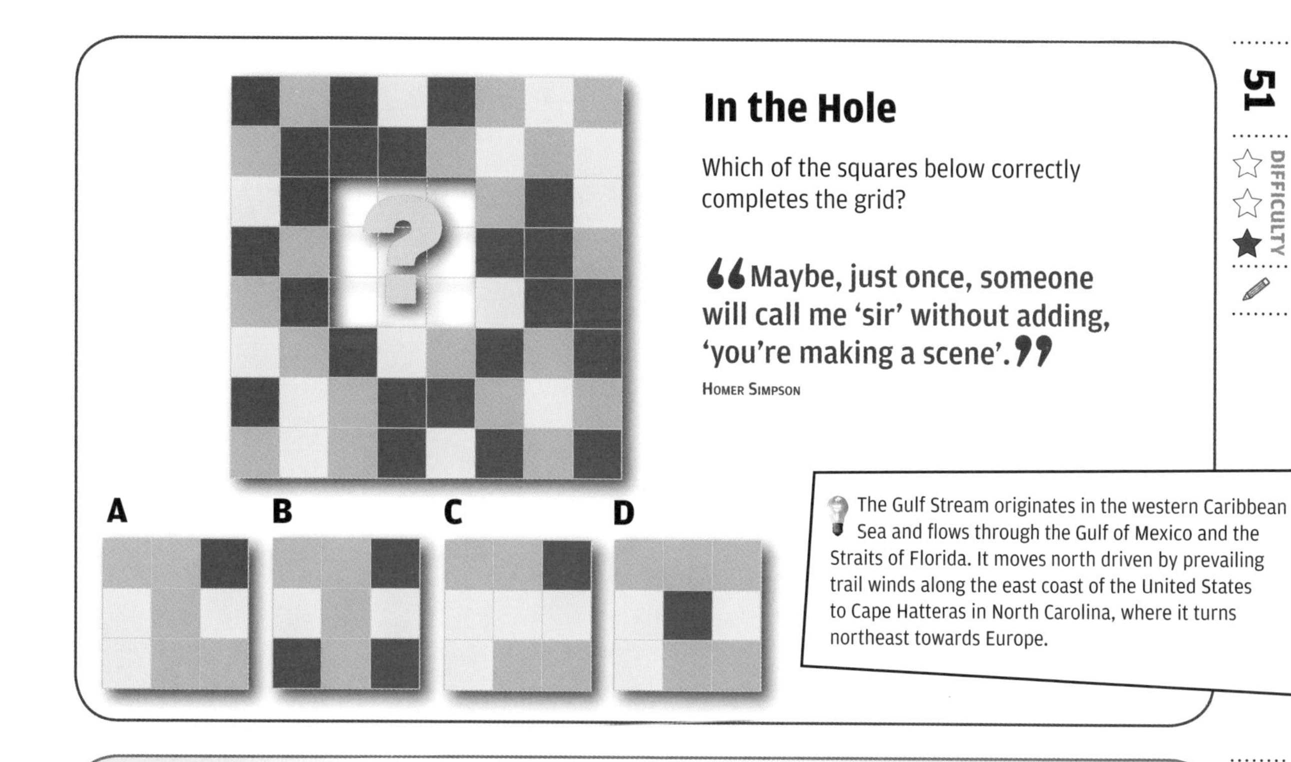

51

DIFFICULTY ☆☆★

In the Hole

Which of the squares below correctly completes the grid?

“Maybe, just once, someone will call me ‘sir’ without adding, ‘you’re making a scene’.”

HOMER SIMPSON

The Gulf Stream originates in the western Caribbean Sea and flows through the Gulf of Mexico and the Straits of Florida. It moves north driven by prevailing trail winds along the east coast of the United States to Cape Hatteras in North Carolina, where it turns northeast towards Europe.

52

DIFFICULTY ☆★★

Jumbled Jigsaw

Which of the four pieces below can complete the jigsaw and make a perfect square?

A B C D E F G H

“Blessed is he who expects nothing for he shall never be disappointed.”

JONATHAN SWIFT

In 1954, Ann Hodge from Alabama, USA, was struck by a four kilogram meteorite which crashed through her ceiling and struck her after bouncing off her radio leaving her badly bruised. It was the first recorded incidence of a human being struck by a meteorite.

53 DIFFICULTY

Knight's Move

Find an empty square in the grid that is one chess knight's move away from a blue, red and yellow circle. A knight's move is an 'L' shape – two squares sideways, up or down in any direction, followed by one square to the left or right.

> **"My loathings are simple: stupidity, oppression, crime, cruelty and soft music."**
> VLADIMIR NABOKOV

The word 'checkmate' comes from the Persian phrase 'Shah Mat', which means 'the King is dead'.

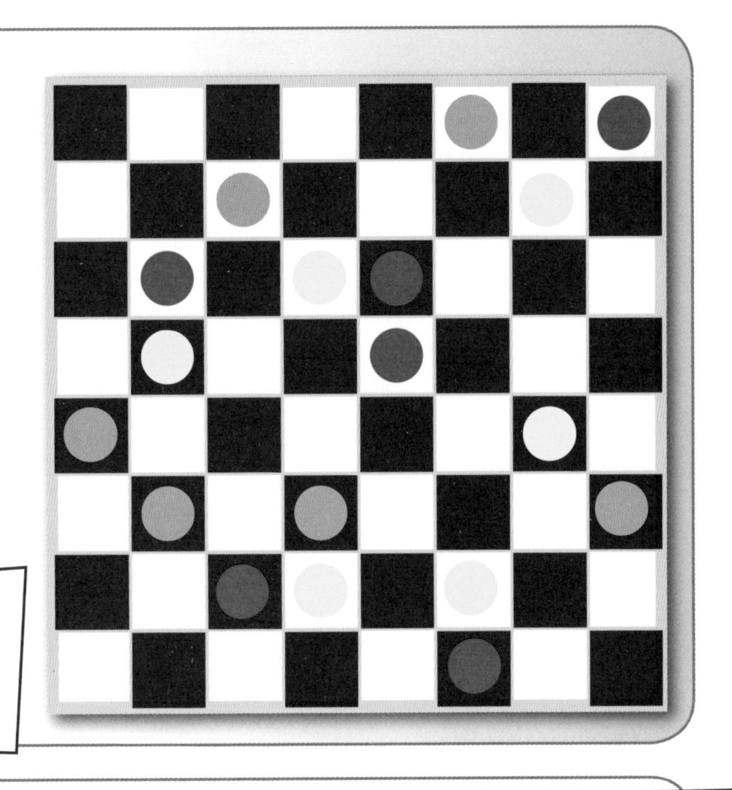

54 DIFFICULTY

Centre of Attention

What numbers should appear in the hubs of these number wheels?

There are three sovereign countries that are completely surrounded by other countries: Lesotho (South Africa), San Marino and the Vatican City (both Italy).

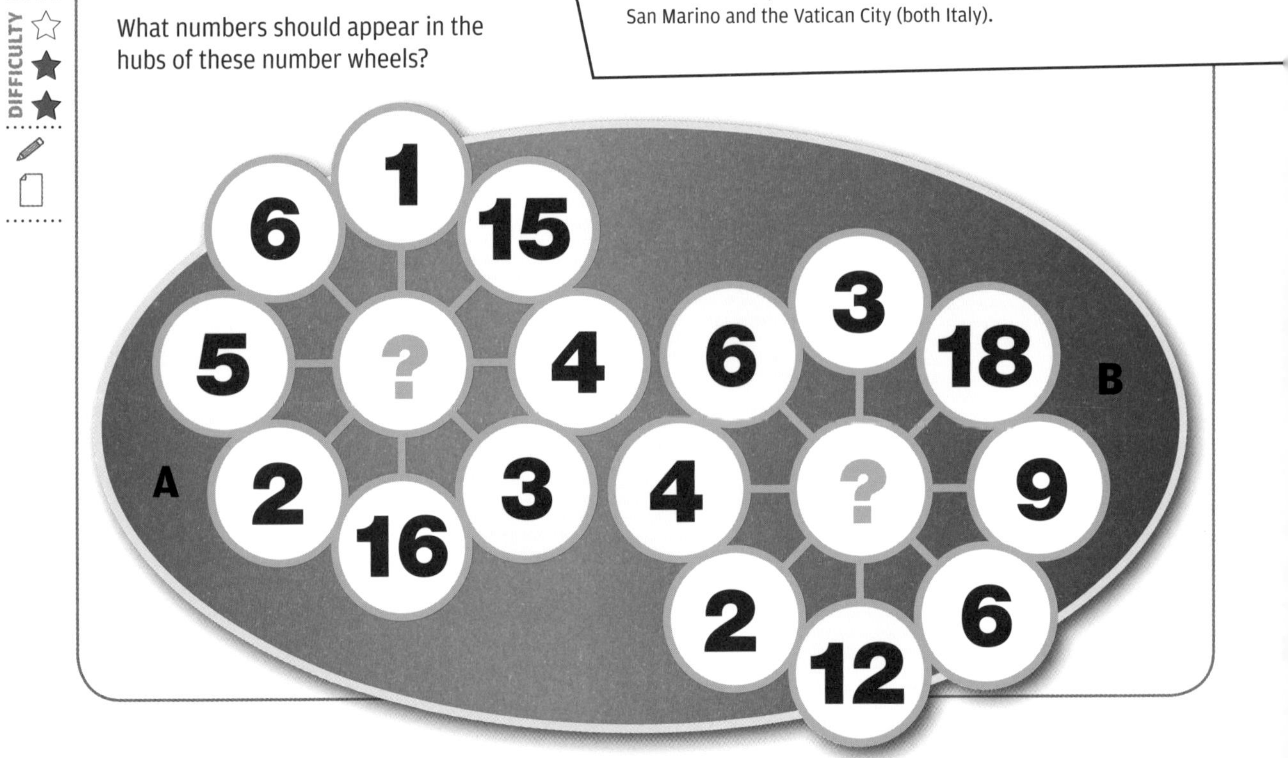

55 DIFFICULTY

Squared Off

B			D		
				E	
	C			F	A

Complete the grid so that every row and column, and every outlined area, contains the letters A, B, C, D, E and F.

“Occasionally he stumbled over the truth, but hastily picked himself up and carried on as if nothing had happened.” Stanley Baldwin

A Motorola telecommunications engineer was the first person to make a call using a cellular phone. On a Manhattan street on 3 April 1973 he called a friend who worked for a rival company to let him know they'd made the breakthrough.

56 DIFFICULTY

Black Out

2		3		2			1
			2		2	3	
	4	1		1			3
			1			5	
4		4			3		
		6			3		3
				5			
1	3		4			2	0

The numbers in some of the squares in the grid indicate the exact number of black squares that should surround it. Shade these squares until all the numbers are surrounded by the correct number of black squares.

“Have a nice day, dear. Don't drive over any mines or anything.” Basil Fawlty

The longest acceptance speech in Academy Award history was delivered by Greer Garson in 1943 upon winning Best Actress for *Mrs Miniver*. It lasted five minutes and 30 seconds.

Number Loopy

Connect adjacent dots with either horizontal or vertical lines to create a continuous unbroken loop which never crosses over itself. Some, but not all of the boxes are numbered. The numbers in these boxes tell you how many sides of that box are used by your unbroken line.

2	2		2	3
	3	1	2	
2				2
3	2		3	
3	1	2		2

“I have but one lamp by which my feet are guided, and that is the lamp of experience. I know no way of judging of the future but by the past.” Edward Gibbon

Mechanical Matrix

Traction engine mechanic Bert Willis has discovered that he has been delivered too many parts. He knows eight of the parts that he definitely needs but can you assist him in working out which of the four boxed figures completes the set?

“The government solution to a problem is usually as bad as the problem.” Milton Friedman

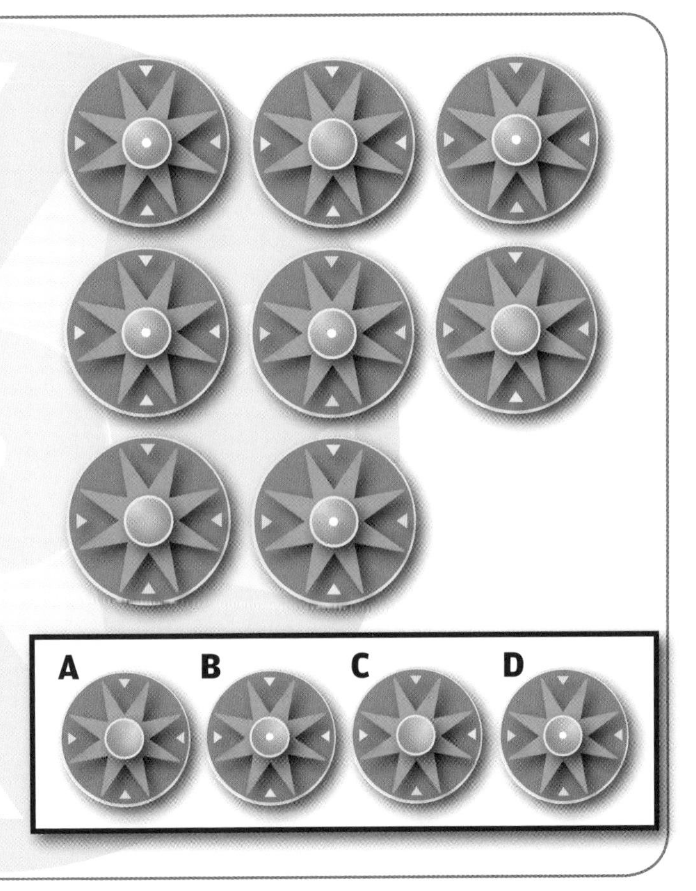

Clarence Birdseye conceived the principle of frozen food in 1930 after watching Eskimos catching fish in temperatures of -50˚F (-45˚C).

The Finns are the world's greatest coffee drinkers, consuming on average 11.4 kilograms every year per person.

59

DIFFICULTY

Magic Squares

18	13	14

Complete the square using nine consecutive numbers, so that all rows, columns and diagonals add up to the same total.

"I believe in equality for everyone – except reporters and photographers." MOHANDAS GHANDI

60

DIFFICULTY

Find the Way

The arrows indicate whether a number in a box is greater or smaller than an adjacent number. Complete the grid so that all rows and columns contain the numbers 1 to 5.

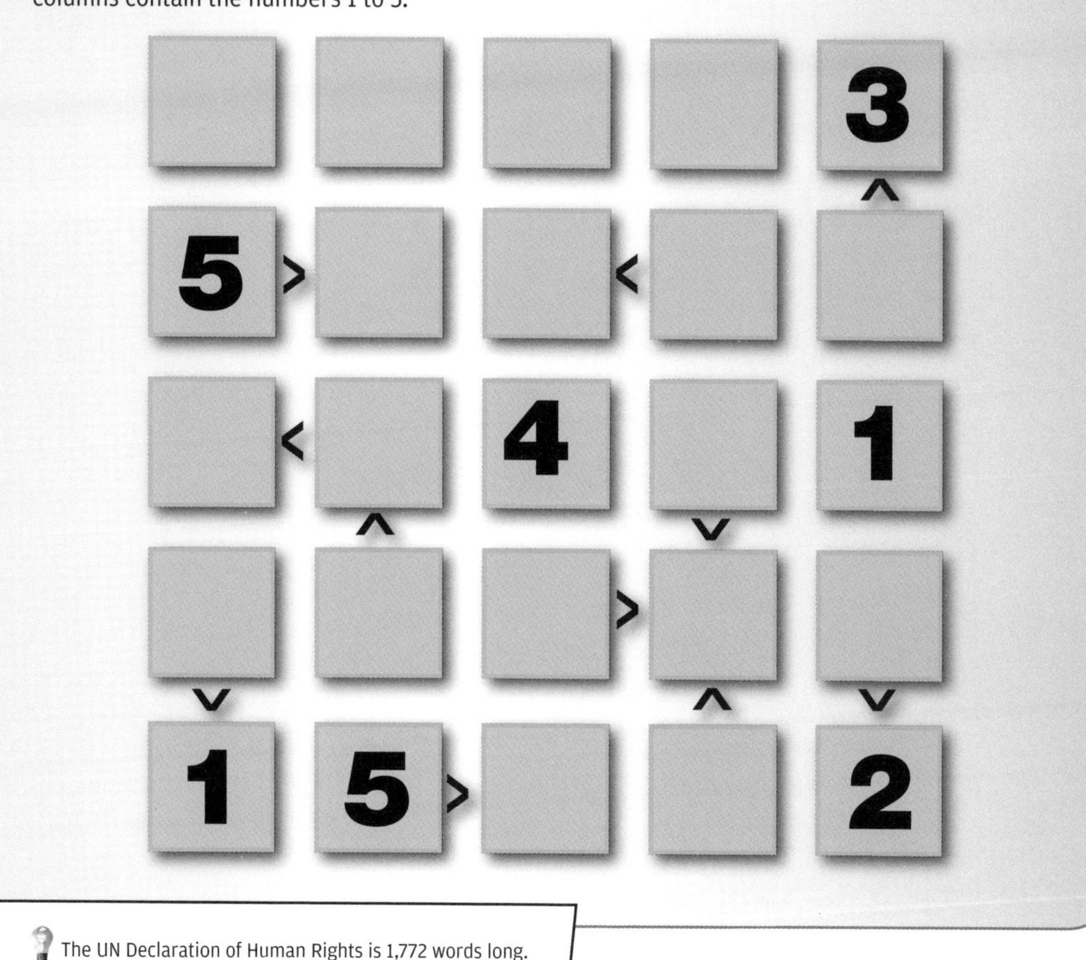

The UN Declaration of Human Rights is 1,772 words long.

61

DIFFICULTY ★★★

Sudoku

Complete the grid so that all rows and columns, and each outlined block of nine squares, contain the numbers 1, 2, 3, 4, 5, 6, 7, 8 and 9 once only.

“Acting is merely the art of keeping a large group of people from coughing.”

Ralph Richardson

						5	4	3
2		6		3			7	
7				6	9		1	
9				2		3		
	4		5		8			2
6		7	8			1		
					3			4
8			6	1				9

62

DIFFICULTY ☆★★

Picture Logic

The numbers by each row and column describe black squares and groups of black squares that are adjoining. Colour in all the black squares and a six number combination will be revealed.

“Manners are especially the need of the plain. The pretty can get away with anything.”

Evelyn Waugh

The most expensive single bottle of wine ever sold was a bottle of 1787 Château Lafite from the cellar of Thomas Jefferson, which sold at Christie's London, for £105,000 in December 1985.

Column clues (top to bottom, left to right):

					1					
					1					
1	1				1	1			1	
1	1			3	1	3			1	
1	1	5		1	1	1		5	1	5
1	1	5		5	1	3		1	1	5

Row clues (left to right, top to bottom):

	3	3	3
1	1	1	1
	3	3	3
	1	1	1
	3	3	3
	3	3	3
	1	1	1
	1	3	1
1	1	1	1
	1	3	1

?

Map Attack

This map can only be coloured in with three colours - blue, yellow and green. Assuming no two adjacent areas can be coloured the same, what colour will the area containing the question mark be?

“Speak softly and carry a big stick.” THEODORE ROOSEVELT

Regarded as the world's longest motorable road, the Pan-American Highway runs for 15,000 miles from Fairbanks, Alaska, USA, to Brasilia, Brazil.

64

DIFFICULTY

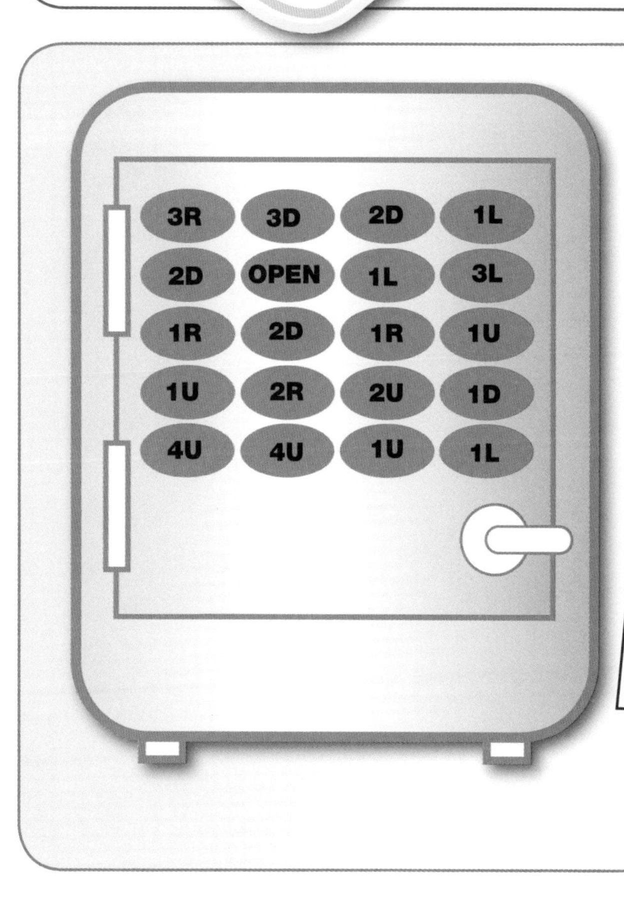

Safecracker

To open the safe, all the buttons must be pressed in the correct order before the ‘open’ button is pressed. What is the first button you must press in your sequence?

“No people is wholly civilized where a distinction is drawn between stealing an office and stealing a purse.”
THEODORE ROOSEVELT

The Ivy League is made up of the north eastern universities of Brown, Columbia, Cornell, Dartmouth, Harvard, Princeton, Pennsylvania and Yale.

65

DIFFICULTY

Big Pot Bonanza

Mac, Jack and Zac are playing poker. They each won a big pot with their biggest hands of the night, but can you work out their surnames, and then who won how much, with which hand?

- Mac won $250 with his biggest hand, which wasn't four of a kind.
- Brunson had the flush and took more than $100 from Zac with it.
- The $100 pot was won by a full house, but not by Chan or Zac.

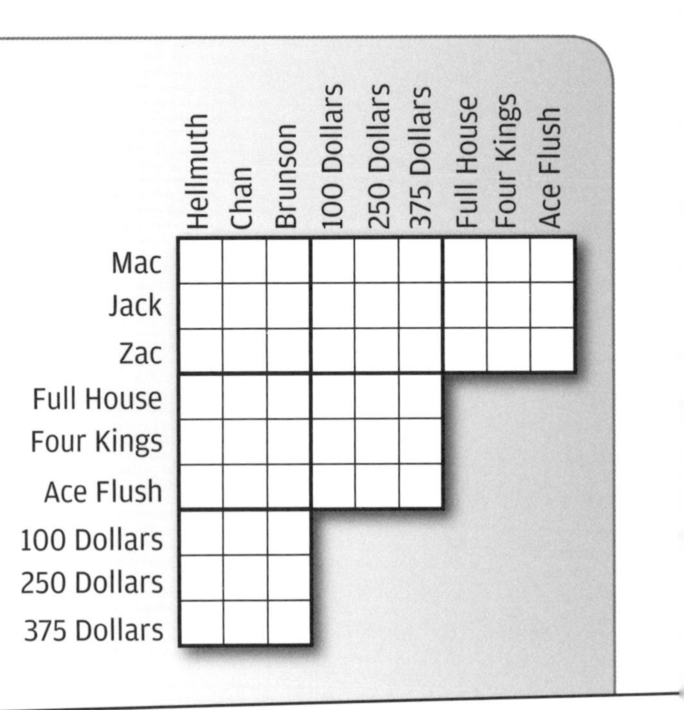

Despite being raised as a Quaker, Richard Nixon was a keen poker player during his two years in the US Navy, and he even used a portion of his winnings to fund his first foray into professional politics in 1946 when he won a Congressional seat.

66

DIFFICULTY

Robot Research

Which box contains exactly the right bits to build the robot?

> "My goal is simple. It is a complete understanding of the universe, why it is as it is and why it exists at all." STEPHEN HAWKING

A

B

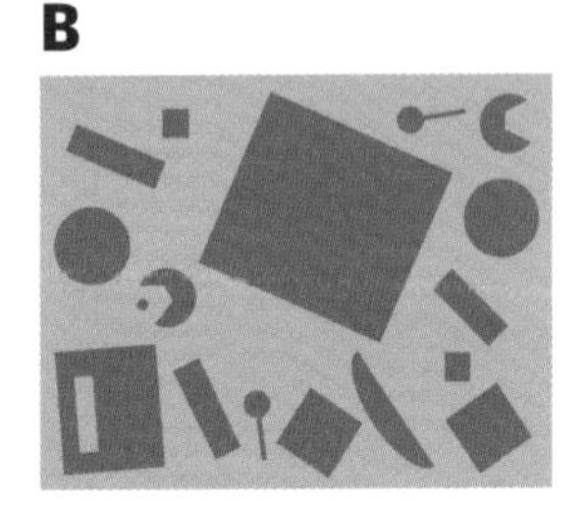

C

In April 2007, the French TGV train broke its own 1990 world train speed record as it reached 574.8 km/h (357.18 mph) under test conditions.

67

DIFFICULTY ★★★

Locate the Letter

A	B	B	B	C	A
B	B	A	C	C	C
A	C	B	A	B	A
B	?	C	B	B	A
A	A	C	B	C	C
C	A	C	C	A	B

What letter, in what colour, should replace the red question mark so that the grid follows a pattern?

“Every artist should be ahead of his time and behind in his rent.”

KINKY FRIEDMAN

In 1895, Émile Levassor driving a Panhard et Levassor won a 1,200 kilometres road race from Paris to Bordeaux and back. The journey took 48 hours and is regarded as the first motor race proper.

68

DIFFICULTY ★★★

Number Mountain

Replace the question marks with numbers so that each pair of blocks adds up to the block directly above them.

“There are many paths to the top of the mountain, but the view is always the same.”

CHINESE PROVERB

178

? ?

? ? ?

27 ? ? 16

11 ? 10 ? 7

? ? ? ? ? 1

New Zealand’s South Island boasts 18 peaks of more than 3,000 metres. The tallest peak is Mount Cook which is 3,754 metres tall.

Same Difference

By examining the relationships of the following shapes, can you identify the next shape?

The first countries to broadcast television were: Germany, the UK and the USA (1936); France and Poland (1937); the Soviet Union (1938); and Japan and Italy (1939).

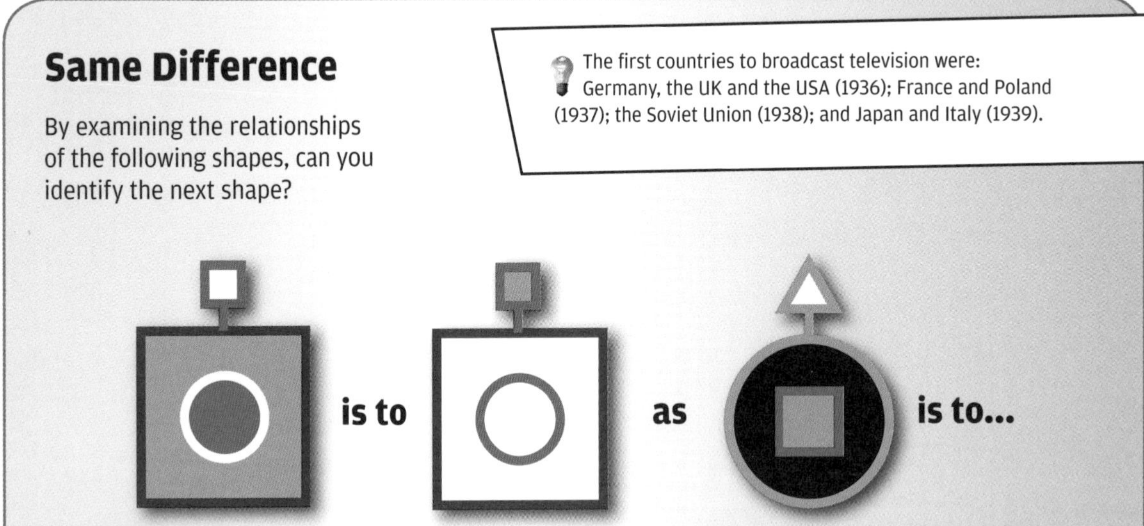

Weigh to Go

The coloured balls represent the numbers 1, 2, 3, 4 and 5. Can you work out which is which, and therefore how many red balls are required to balance the final scale?

“Read not to contradict and confute, nor to believe and take for granted... but to weigh and consider.” Francis Bacon

The first abacus was almost certainly based on a flat stone covered with sand or dust. Words and letters were drawn in the sand; eventually numbers were added and pebbles used to aid calculations. The Babylonians used this dust abacus as early as 2,400 BC.

71

DIFFICULTY

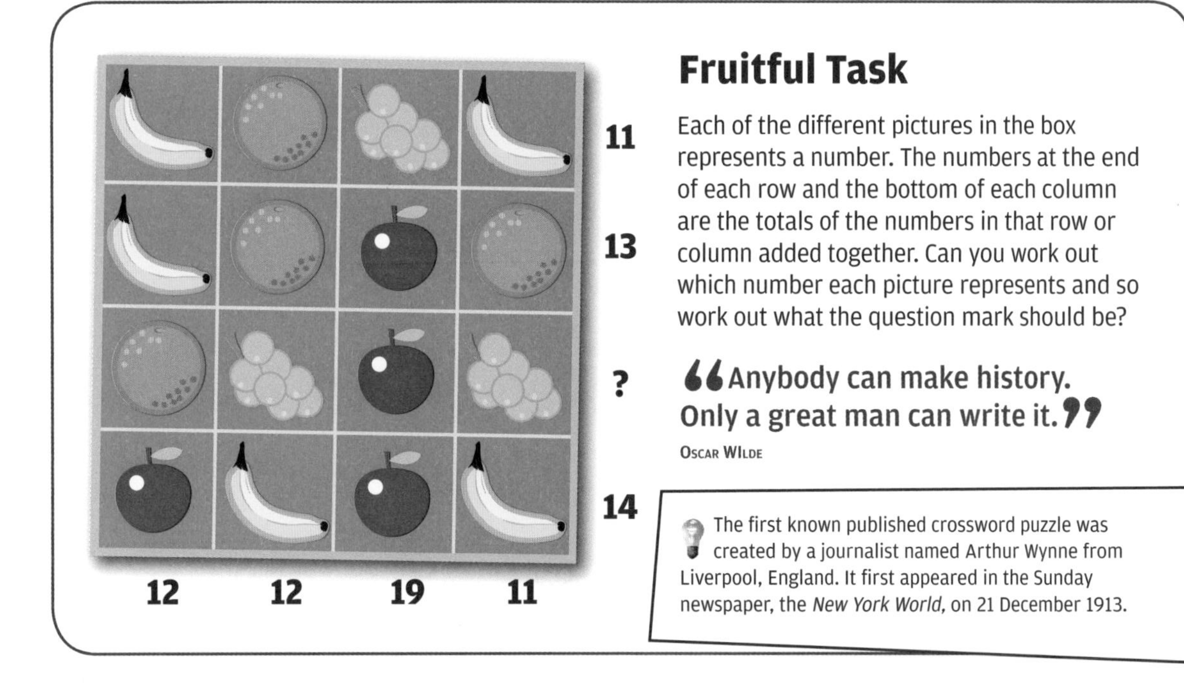

Fruitful Task

Each of the different pictures in the box represents a number. The numbers at the end of each row and the bottom of each column are the totals of the numbers in that row or column added together. Can you work out which number each picture represents and so work out what the question mark should be?

“Anybody can make history. Only a great man can write it.”

Oscar Wilde

The first known published crossword puzzle was created by a journalist named Arthur Wynne from Liverpool, England. It first appeared in the Sunday newspaper, the *New York World*, on 21 December 1913.

72

DIFFICULTY

Grand Prix Puzzle

This racing car is made up of building bricks that are all the same size. Can you work out what percentage of them is grey, blue, black and red?

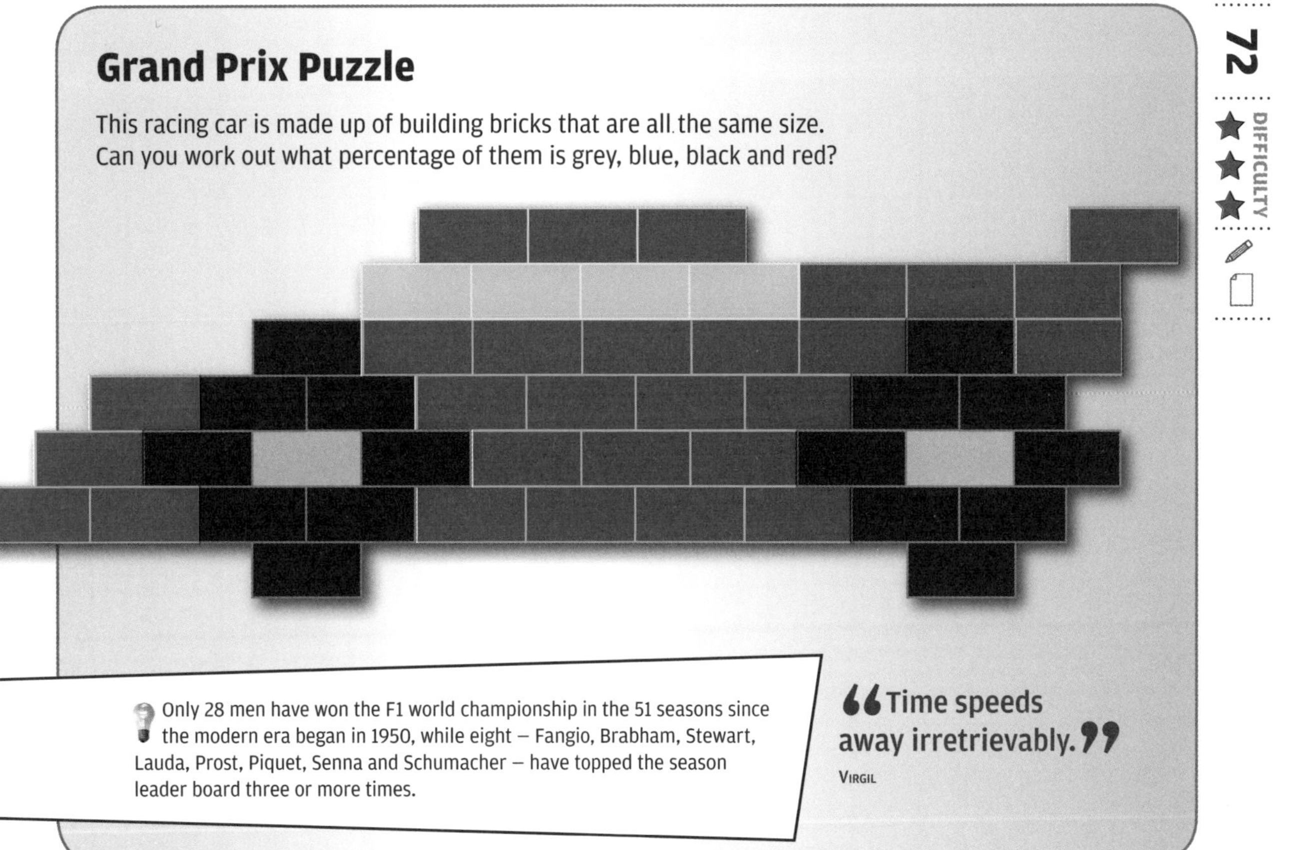

Only 28 men have won the F1 world championship in the 51 seasons since the modern era began in 1950, while eight – Fangio, Brabham, Stewart, Lauda, Prost, Piquet, Senna and Schumacher – have topped the season leader board three or more times.

“Time speeds away irretrievably.”

Virgil

73

DIFFICULTY

View to a Clue

The four squares at the bottom can all be found in the picture grid. Can you track them down? Beware, they may not be the right way up.

"Everything in nature is lyrical in its ideal essence, tragic in its fate, and comic in its existence." George Santayana

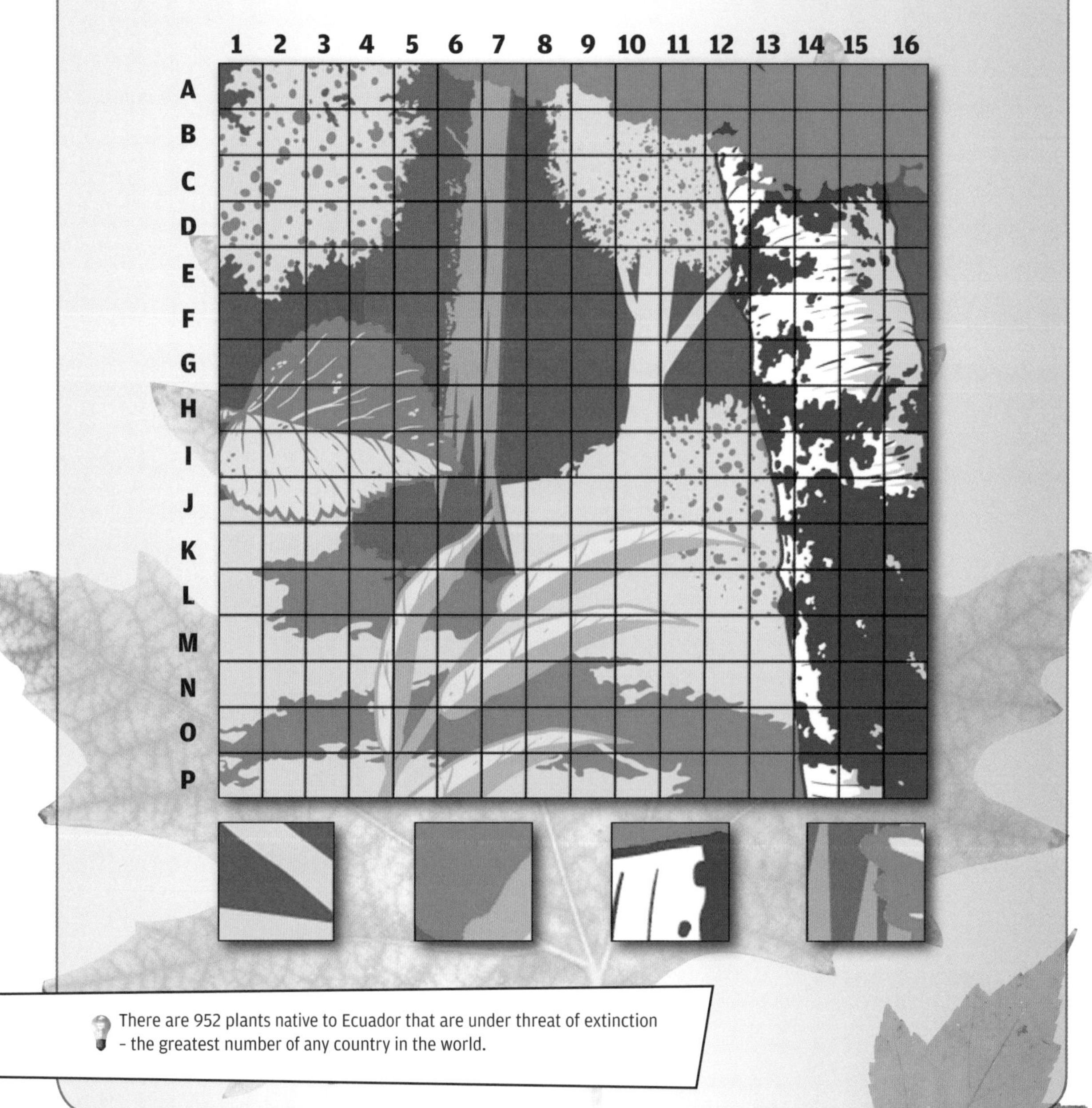

There are 952 plants native to Ecuador that are under threat of extinction – the greatest number of any country in the world.

74

DIFFICULTY ☆☆★

Cubism

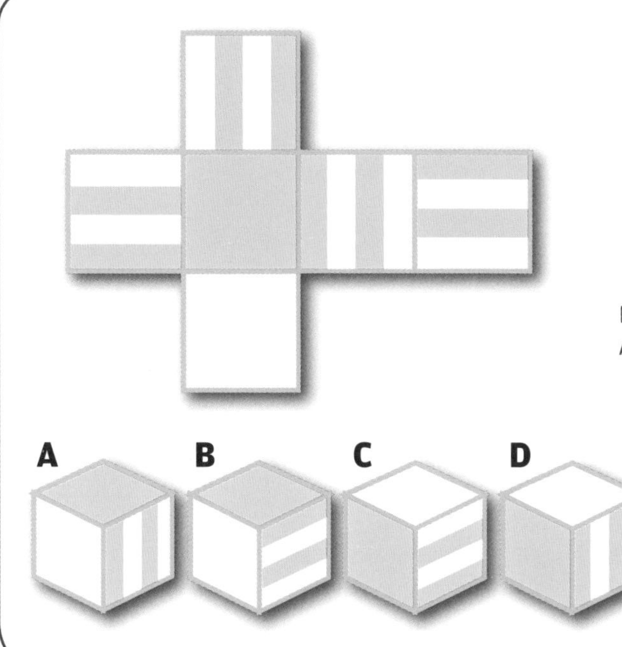

The shape left can be folded to make a cube. Which of the four cubes pictured below could it make?

> **"What people call fate is mostly their own stupidity."**
>
> Arthur Schopenhauer

The British Secret Service Bureau was set up in 1909 in response to the threat posed to the UK's naval ports by spies from imperial Germany. It was renamed MI5 (Military Intelligence, Section 5) in 1916 and again as the Security Service in 1931 - though MI5 is still popularly used today.

75

DIFFICULTY ☆☆★

Do you Remember Me?

Study these images for a minute, cover them up with a sheet of paper and then answer the five questions shown below.

Questions:

1. How many of the men have handkerchiefs that match their ties?
2. How many of the blond men have yellow ties?
3. How many men with red ties have white handkerchiefs?
4. What colour is the background on the man with the green suit?
5. What colour tie has the blond man on the blue background?

On 28 February 1953, Frances Crick walked into The Eagle pub in Cambridge and announced that he and James Watson "had found the secret of life" - the two Cambridge academics had discovered DNA.

76

DIFFICULTY ☆★★

To Follow

In the sequence below, which of the numbered alternatives, A, B, C or D, should replace the question mark?

The first Oxford-Cambridge Boat Race was held in 1829 at the suggestion of two old Harrovians, Charles Merivale (Cambridge) and Charles Wordsworth (Oxford).

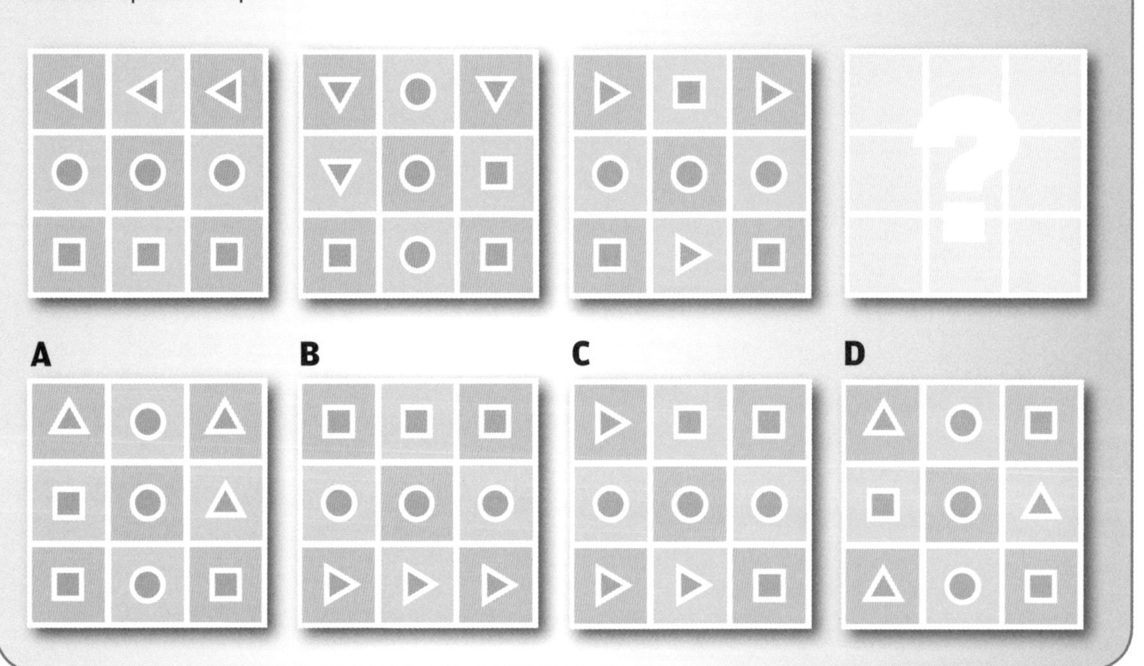

77

DIFFICULTY ☆★★

Dinosaur Dilemma

Can you work out the approximate area that the dinosaur part of this image takes up?

“If size did matter, the dinosaurs would still be alive.” Wendelin Wiedeking

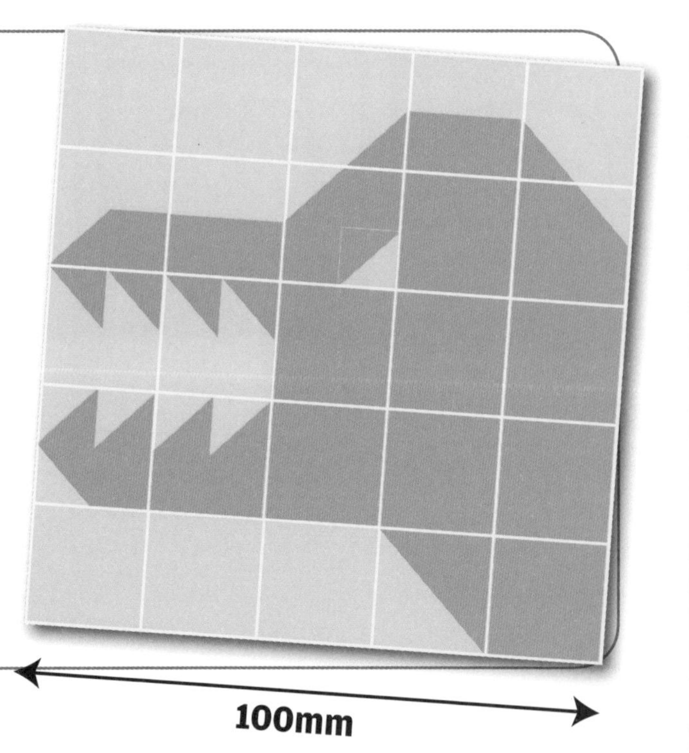

The smallest known dinosaur is the Compsognathus which was the size of a chicken. The largest was the Sauroposeidon, which means 'earthquake god lizard', weighed 60 tonnes and stood 18 metres (60 feet) tall.

All Sewn Up

78

DIFFICULTY ☆★★

Reassemble these torn pieces and you will reveal... What?

"The most happy marriage I can picture or imagine to myself would be the union of a deaf man to a blind woman." S. T. COLERIDGE

The Chinese consider it bad luck to turn a fish over at the table. The superstition is originally attributed to South China's fishing families who believed bad luck would ensue and a fishing boat would capsize if the fish were up-ended.

Cats and Cogs

79

DIFFICULTY ☆☆★

Turn the handle in the indicated direction... Does the cat in the basket go up or down?

"A cat is more intelligent than people believe, and can be taught any crime." MARK TWAIN

80

DIFFICULTY

Fruit Formula

The islands of Zanga, Binoo and Biro Biro export fruit around the world. Can you work out in which sea or ocean the islands are, and which island produces which fruit for which country?

- Zanga is not in the Pacific Ocean, and its mangoes are not exported to the USA.
- Australia imports the coconuts, which are not from Binoo.
- Biro Biro is in the Caribbean.

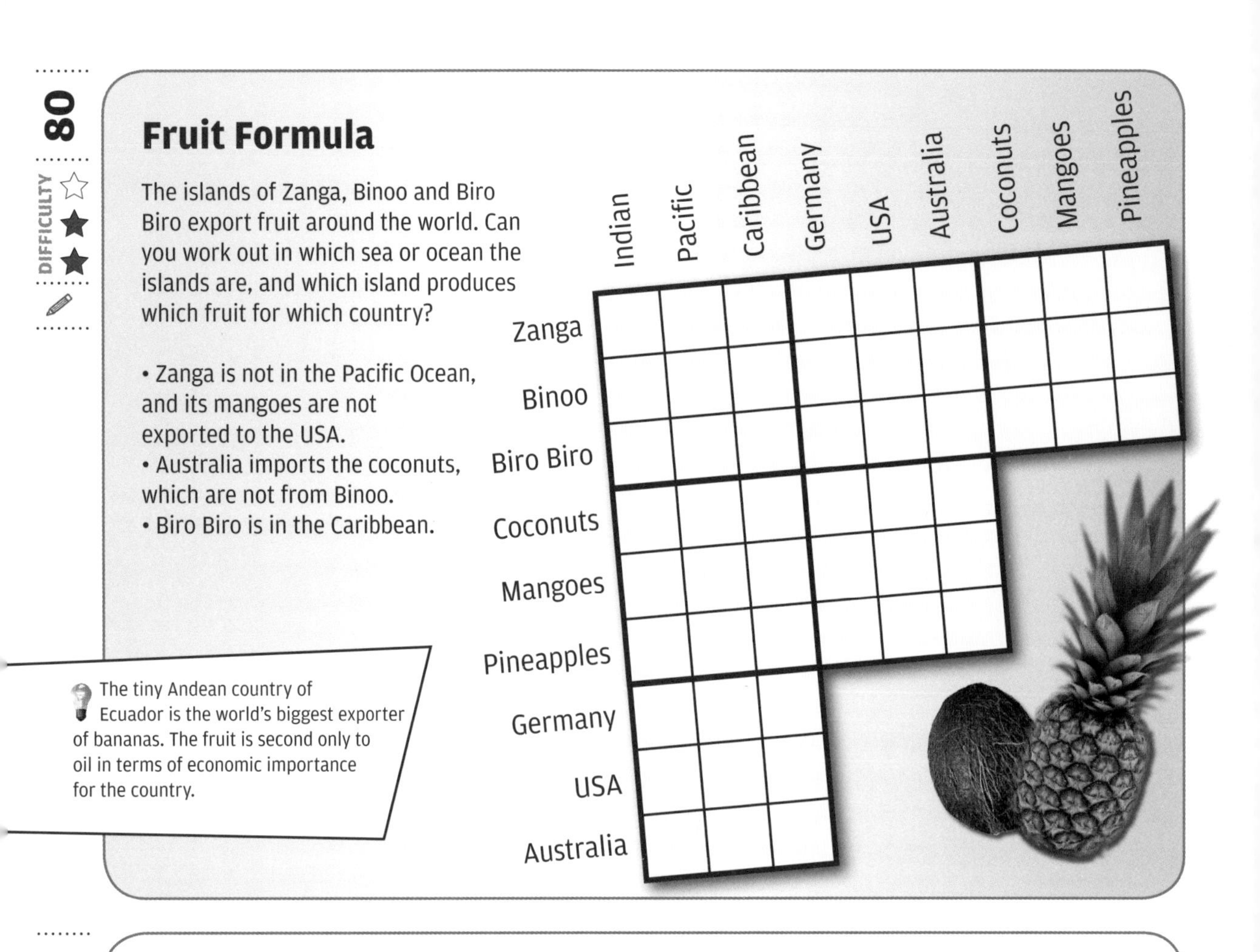

The tiny Andean country of Ecuador is the world's biggest exporter of bananas. The fruit is second only to oil in terms of economic importance for the country.

81

DIFFICULTY

Follow That

The sequence below follows a logical pattern. Can you work out what design should come next?

> "The chief distinction of a diplomat is that he can say no in such a way that it sounds like yes." LESTER BOWLES PEARSON

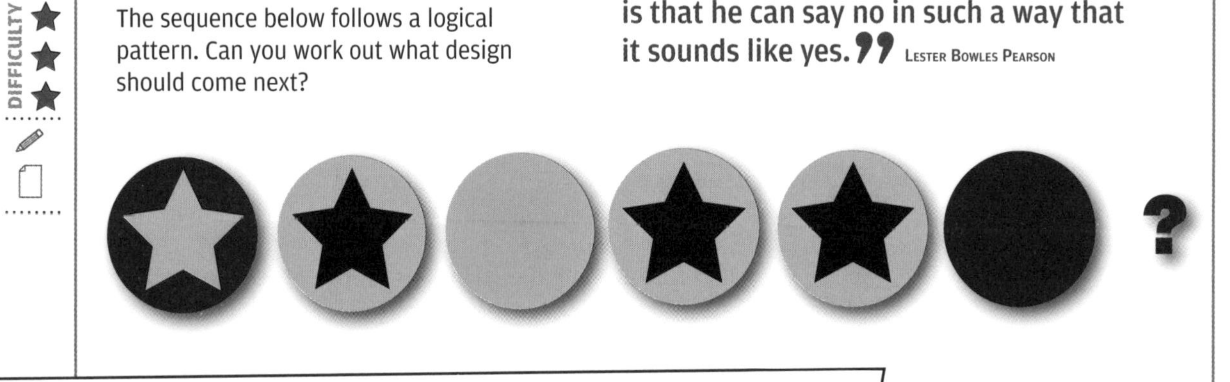

On 16 October 1923, brothers Walt and Roy Disney founded the Walt Disney Company - it was originally known as the Disney Brothers Cartoon Studio.

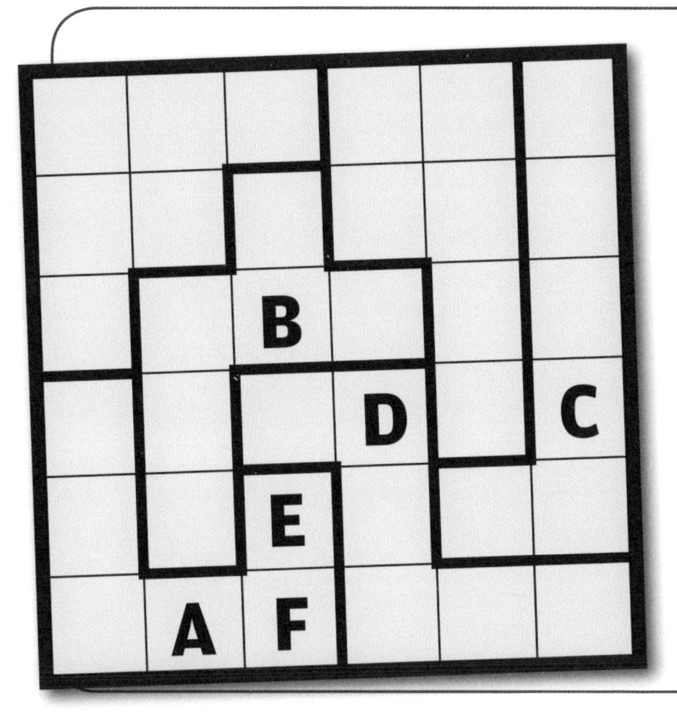

82

DIFFICULTY

Squared Off

Complete the grid so that every row and column, and every outlined area, contains the letters A, B, C, D, E and F.

“In a time of universal deceit, telling the truth becomes a revolutionary act.” GEORGE ORWELL

Mining in the Witwatersrand Basin region of South Africa has unearthed one-third of all the gold ever mined on the planet.

83

DIFFICULTY

Block Party

Assuming all blocks that are not visible from this angle are present, how many blocks have been removed from this 6 x 6 x 6 cube?

“Maybe the most that you can expect from a relationship that goes bad is to come out of it with a few good songs.” MARIANNE FAITHFULL

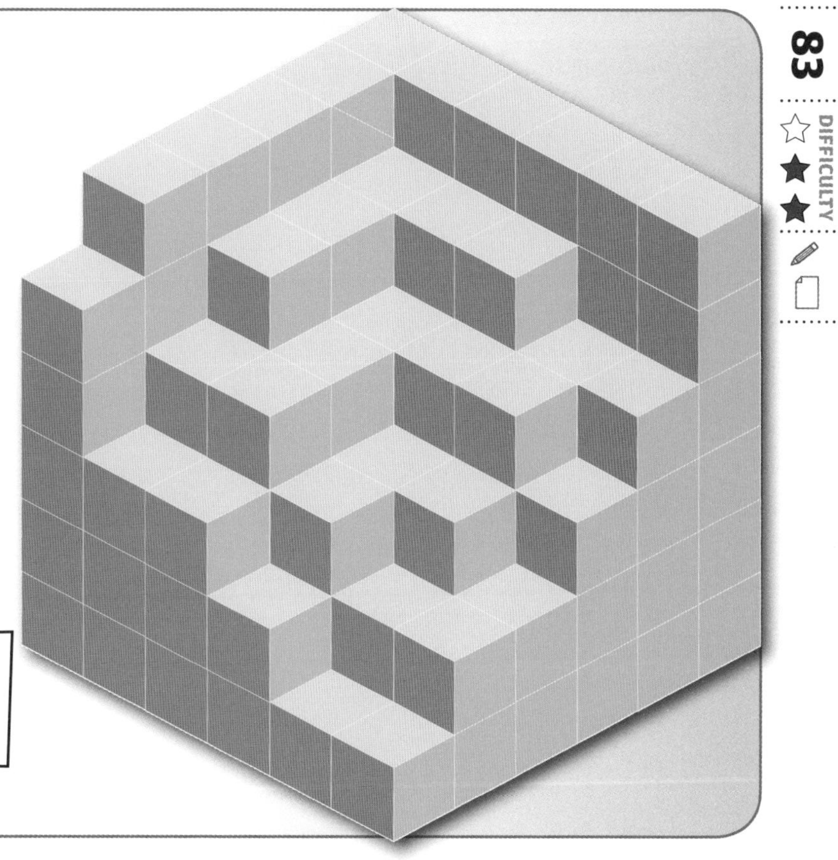

The 2006 US census put the population at 299,398,484. It had risen by 6.4% since 2000.

Boxing Clever

The value of each shape is the number of sides each shape has, multiplied by the number within it. Thus a square containing the number 4 has a value of 16. Find a block of four squares (two squares wide by two squares high) with a total value of exactly 60.

pentagon 5	pentagon 3	hexagon 2	square 5	hexagon 5
pentagon 1	triangle 3	pentagon 2	square 3	triangle 5
square 6	square 2	triangle 4	hexagon 4	triangle 3
square 6	triangle 5	hexagon 3	hexagon 1	hexagon 1
square 4	pentagon 6	pentagon 4	triangle 3	square 5

“I read the newspapers avidly. It is my one form of continuous fiction.” Aneurin Bevan

The world's deepest public house can be found six kilometres south of Johannesburg city centre in what used to be a donkey stable for a thriving gold-mining reef in the 1920s. Known as Shaft 14, it is 226 metres underground.

Gold and Silver

Every gold coin has a silver coin found horizontally or vertically adjacent to it. No silver coin can be in an adjacent square to another silver coin (even diagonally). The numbers by each row and column tell you how many silver coins are there. Can you locate all the silver coins?

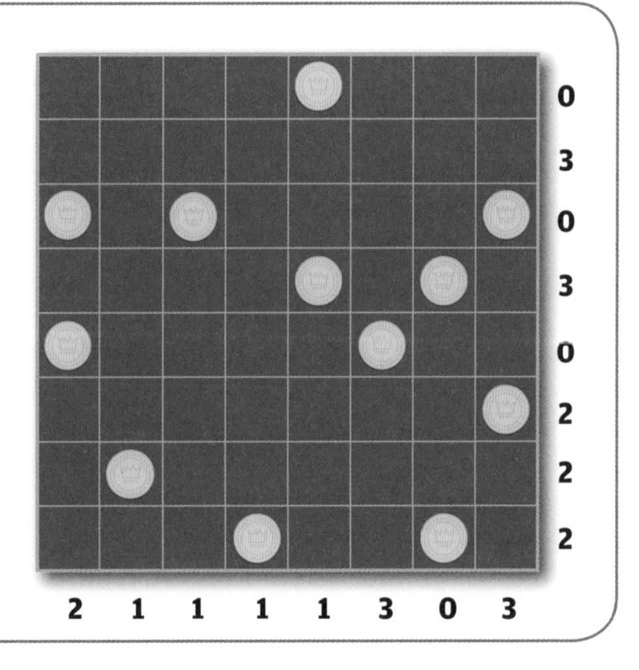

Gold is so malleable that an ounce of gold can be stretched to a length of over 50 miles or beaten into a sheet to cover 100 square feet.

Piecing It Together

Which four of the pieces below can complete the jigsaw and make a perfect square?

> “Sex appeal is 50 percent what you've got and 50 percent what people think you've got.” SOPHIA LOREN

King Henry III became ruler of England in 1216 when he was just nine years old and ruled until his death in 1272. During his reign a polar bear was kept at the Tower of London. It was a gift from King Haakon IV of Norway.

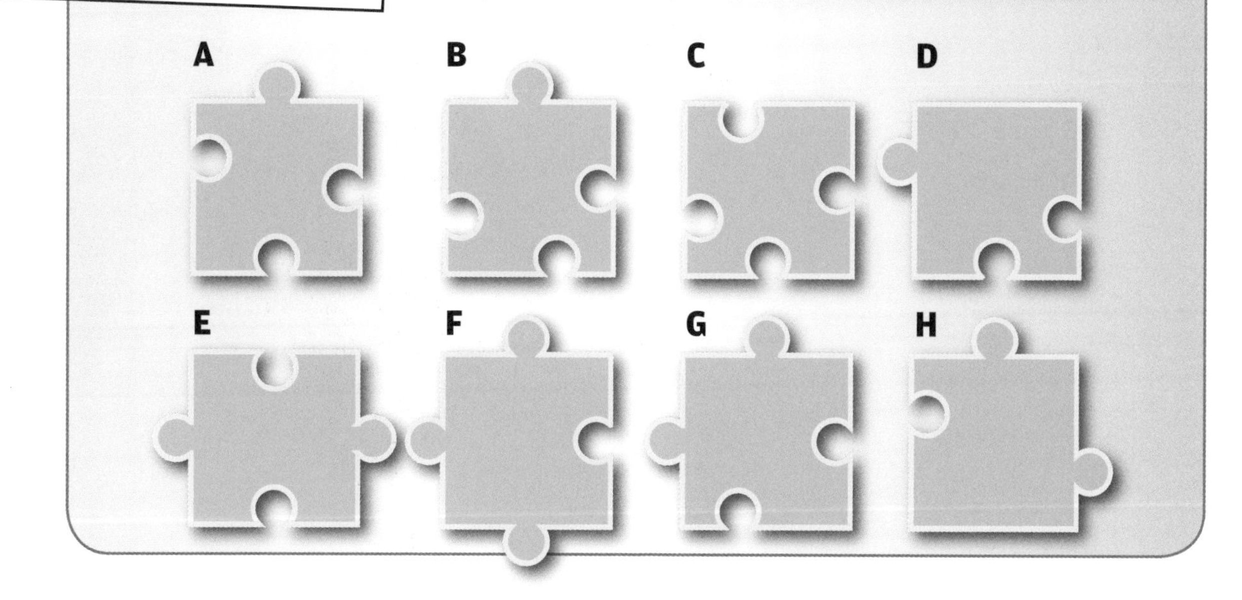

87 Seeing Double

All these icons appear twice in the box except one. Can you spot the singleton?

"If I have seen farther than others, it is because I was standing on the shoulders of giants." SIR ISAAC NEWTON

President Theodore Roosevelt was not only the first serving President to ride in an automobile, but also the first serving President to travel outside the country when he visited Panama in November 1906.

88 DIFFICULTY

88 Make the Cut

Cut two straight lines through this shape to create three shapes that are identical.

"A national political campaign is better than the best circus ever heard of, with a mass baptism and a couple of hangings thrown in." H. L. MENCKEN

The word 'April' is derived from the Latin 'aperie' which translates as 'to open' and was used to describe the first flowering of spring.

The Next Step

Which of the four boxed figures completes the sequence?

"Standing in the middle of the road is very dangerous; you get knocked down by the traffic from both sides." MARGARET THATCHER

The world's first traffic light was installed outside the Houses of Parliament in London, England, in 1868. At this point the only traffic was pedestrian or horse-drawn buggies. It was a revolving gas lantern with red and green signals. Unfortunately the light exploded in 1869, injuring a policeman.

90

DIFFICULTY ★★★

Super Sudoku

Complete the grid so that all rows and columns, and each outlined block of nine squares, contain the numbers 1, 2, 3, 4, 5, 6, 7, 8 and 9.

“I believe that every human has a finite number of heartbeats. I don’t intend to waste any of mine running around doing exercises.”

Neil Armstrong

	7				5		4	
			1		6			
2			3			1		8
		5				3		
			4	1				
3		9			7			6
7			8		4		3	
		2		9		5		
	5		6				8	1

As a boy, cult film director David Lynch attained the rank of Eagle Scout – the highest in the US Boy Scout movement. On his 15th birthday Lynch, as an Eagle Scout, served as an usher at the inauguration of President John F. Kennedy.

91

DIFFICULTY ☆★★

Knitty Gritty

Old Mother Jones loves to knit when she’s worried. This month her daughter is learning to drive and she has produced 238 scarves, 71 pom-pom hats and 41 beanie hats. As a percentage of total production, how much of her output were hats?

“In every conceivable manner, the family is link to our past, bridge to our future.” Alex Haley

One of the earliest known examples of knitting was finely decorated cotton socks found in Egypt at the end of the first millennium AD. The first knitting trade guild was started in Paris in 1527.

Complete the Masterpiece

92

DIFFICULTY

The painting Four Suns Over Tokyo is in three colours only: purple, yellow and green. No two areas of the same colour border each other. What colour is the top right hand corner?

“It’s amazing what you can do with an E in A-level art, twisted imagination and a chainsaw.”

Damien Hirst

?

The amount of energy poured onto the earth from the sun every 15 minutes is roughly equivalent to the earth’s electricity needs for a year.

Black Out

93

DIFFICULTY

3			3		3		1
		4		3			2
	4		2		3	4	
	3	2			2		3
4		3	1	3		4	
				2		4	
	4		2		3		2
1		1			2	2	

The numbers in some squares in the grid indicate the exact number of black squares that should surround it. Shade these squares until all the numbers are surrounded by the correct number of black squares.

“Darkness is only driven out with light, not more darkness.”

Martin Luther King Jr

94

DIFFICULTY ★

Cowboy Line-Up

Hoss McGrew is wanted in six counties for rustling chickens. He always wears a hat with no band on it, a waistcoat and a neckerchief... Can you pick him out of the line up?

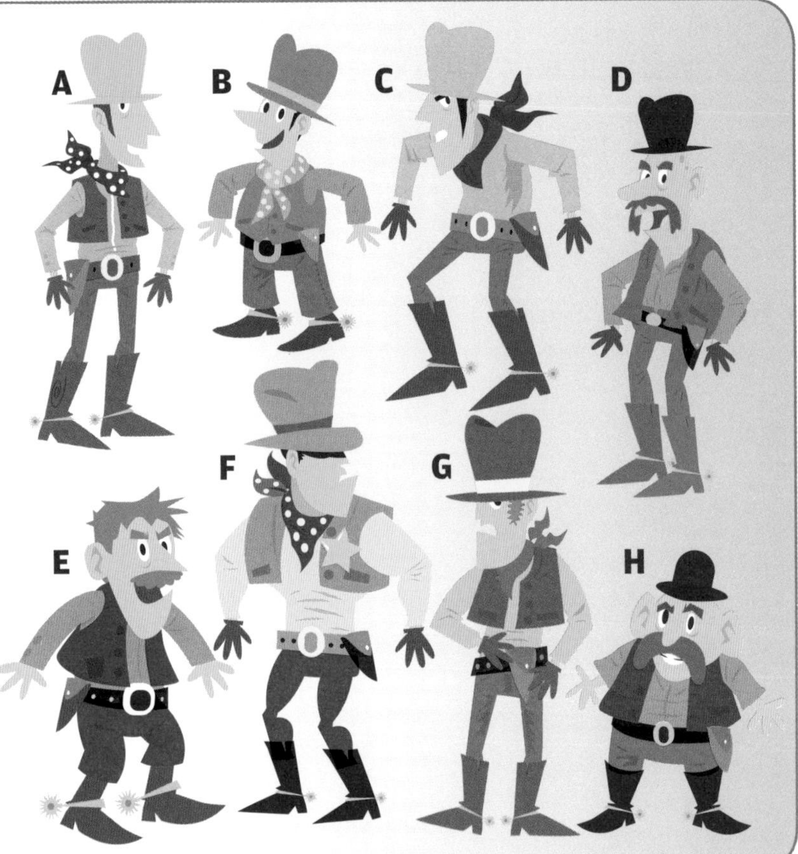

"Love is the ultimate outlaw. It just won't adhere to any rules. The most any of us can do is sign on as its accomplice." Tom Watson

There were 17,576 possible rotor settings on the original Enigma code machine used in World War II to break secret codes.

95

DIFFICULTY ★★

Coming Together

These seven pieces can be assembled into a green square with what on it?

"No matter how old a mother is, she watches her middle-aged children for signs of improvement." Florida Scott-Maxwell

96

DIFFICULTY

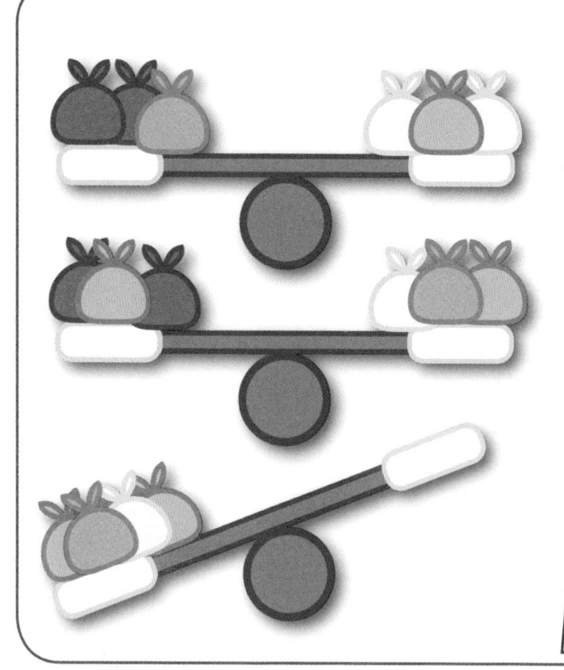

Level Loads

The coloured sacks - green, blue, brown, yellow and black - represent the numbers 1, 2, 3, 4 and 5. Can you work out which is which, and therefore how many black sacks are required to balance the bottom seesaw?

“There is always a heavy demand for fresh mediocrity. In every generation the least cultivated taste has the largest appetite.” Paul Gauguin

The Russian KGB was created in 1954. At its peak, it was the world's largest secret-police and espionage organization. After playing a part in a failed coup attempt to overthrow Mikhail Gorbachev it lost influence and was finally dissolved when the Soviet Union collapsed.

97

DIFFICULTY

Car Countdown

Each of the different pictures in the box represents a number. The numbers at the end of each row and the bottom of each column are the totals of the numbers in that row or column added together. Can you work out which number each picture represents and so work out what the question mark should be?

25

23

16

14

18 15 ? 23

“The best car safety device is a rear-view mirror with a cop in it.” Dudley Moore

There are over 600 million motor vehicles in the world today. If present trends continue, the number of cars on the earth will double in the next 30 years.

Loopy Numbers

Connect adjacent dots with either horizontal or vertical lines to create a continuous unbroken loop which never crosses over itself. Some but not all of the boxes are numbered. The numbers in these boxes tell you how many sides of that box are used by your unbroken line.

3	3	2	2	2
		1		
2	3		2	3
	2	1		2
3		2		3

Until 9 July 2007, the Argentine capital Buenos Aires had not seen snow for 89 years.

99

DIFFICULTY

Make the Cut

Can you fold a straight line through this shape to create two shapes that are identical?

“It took man thousands of years to put words down on paper, and his lawyers still wish he wouldn’t.” MIGNON MCLAUGHLIN

Dr James Naismith, a gym instructor from Springfield, Massachusetts, invented basketball as a way of keeping his students active and competitive during the break between the American football and baseball seasons in 1891-92.

100

DIFFICULTY ☆☆★

What's the Difference?

Can you spot 10 differences between these two pictures of a bird relaxing on a Sunday morning?

Ernest Hemingway was a civilian in Cuba during World War II, but he added surveillance capabilities to his own private boat so he could guard the waters against German submarines.

101 DIFFICULTY ★★★

Star Corner

Use the corner stars to make the central number the same way in all three cases. What number should replace the question mark?

“We make war that we may live in peace.” ARISTOTLE

Scientists have developed a currency durable enough to be used in space in anticipation of future space tourism. Designed in the UK, it is called the Quasi Universal Intergalactic Denomination, or Quid.

Reach for the Stars

Can you find three perfect five-pointed stars in this colourful collection?

“A man gazing on the stars is proverbially at the mercy of the puddles in the road.”
ALEXANDER SMITH

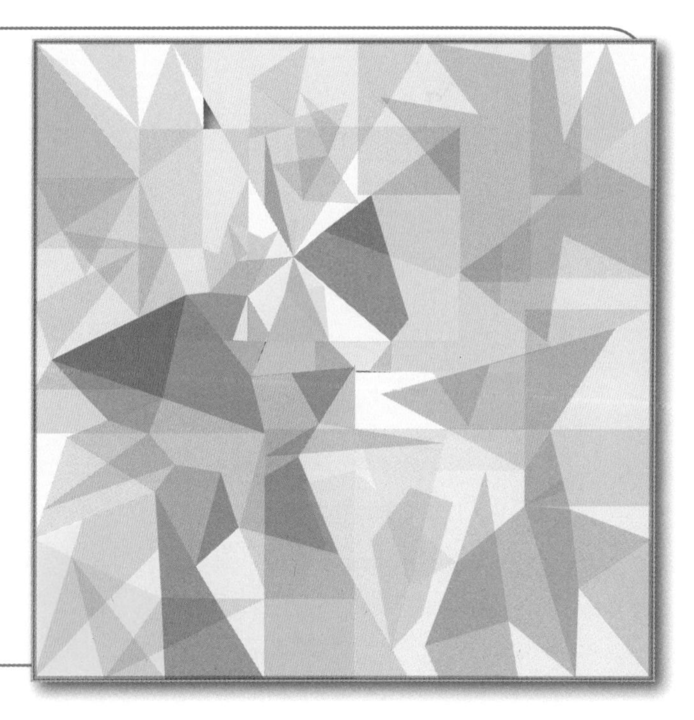

The amount of power transmitted by the Galileo spacecraft's radio is about the same amount used by a refrigerator light bulb - about 20 watts.